intraclass correlation

intraclass correlation and the analysis of variance

ERNEST A. HAGGARD

Professor of Psychology, College of Medicine
University of Illinois

WITH AN APPENDIX BY HARI C. GUPTA

THE DRYDEN PRESS, INC · NEW YORK

© 1958 by The Dryden Press, Inc.
Library of Congress Catalog Card Number: 57-14533
All rights reserved. For information address
The Dryden Press, Inc., 110 West 57th Street, New York 19, N.Y.
Printed in the United States of America

To students of the behavioral sciences
who, by their work,
may help to build a better world

PREFACE

Some time ago I planned to write a short note, of one or two pages, indicating that the coefficient of intraclass correlation should be used to summarize certain types of psychological data. At the time my knowledge of this coefficient was limited to the brief discussions found in a few textbooks. But then I came across an article by J. A. Harris published in 1913, in which he proposed a computational method designed to simplify the calculation of intraclass correlations. The method was based on his finding that the total variance of a set of scores could be partitioned and that the coefficient of intraclass correlation could be expressed as a ratio of two variances.

This computational short-cut discovered by Harris did not result in any sudden increase in the popularity or refinement of the correlation coefficient which interested him. Rather, it was used most profitably by R. A. Fisher along rather different lines, in developing small sample theory and the analysis of variance. In the last few years a number of fundamental advances have been made in the theory of analysis of variance models, and it is just these advances which have, in turn, made it possible to realize the generality of the intraclass correlation concept.

In this book I have tried to integrate this generalized correlation concept with modern theory of analysis of variance. By and large, the aspects of this theory which I have included are pretty well settled, or at least they are generally accepted by statisticians today. I have also tried to indicate the application of this theory to some practical problems which the behavioral scientist has to deal with in his day-to-day work. In organizing this material I have tried to keep in mind the student with relatively little knowledge of statistical theory and methods. For this reason, the first five chapters deal in general with the formal properties of the coefficient of intraclass correlation, and the last three chapters deal with some of its applications. Furthermore, new concepts, examples, and computations are gradually introduced and built upon in subsequent sections. This organization may not be suitable for everyone. For example, the material in Chapter III should make more sense if the advanced student begins with Chapter V than if these chapters are read in the usual order.

The present content of this book has passed through a series of phases or stages. In each instance, formulations of specific properties or the general approach seemed to be entirely satisfactory at the time. However, at each stage there emerged previously unseen incongruities within the total framework, or it became apparent that gaps existed which should be filled by the discussion of specific relationships of the concept with other statistical approaches and techniques. At this point a new organization had to be worked out which, for a while at least, seemed to be obvious or even necessary. (If intraclass correlation had not remained practically dormant for thirty years, it would not have been necessary to go through a number of reformulations—nor would the job of doing it have been so fascinating.) Consequently, it is not to be supposed that the present version is exhaustive and without gaps and shortcomings; in fact, several sections, such as a discussion of intraclass correlation and factor analysis, have been omitted because a good deal of additional work needs to be done on them. But to be perfectly honest, what started out to be a brief note has already taken so much longer than I originally planned that I have decided to call a halt, at least for the time being. This decision is not made without mixed feelings, however, since the elegance inherent in statistical reasoning provides its own special type of satisfaction.

This work would not have been possible without the help of many friends and colleagues. Two of my former students have contributed substantially to the present form of this book. As the manuscript progressed through its middle stages, Hari C. Gupta and I spent many hours discussing and reformulating matters of detail and general approach. A good deal of the material in Chapters I to IV was influenced by his thinking, and the proofs in Appendix II are given essentially as he prepared them. To R. Darrell Bock I am indebted for his many valuable suggestions throughout the book, especially in connection with Chapters V to VII. Many other persons also contributed helpful criticisms and suggestions at various times. Among those to whom I am thus indebted are Jack Block, Lee J. Cronbach, Allen L. Edwards, Lyle V. Jones, Jane Loevinger, Eli S. Marks, Quinn McNemar, Douglas More, and Julian C. Stanley. I also wish to express my appreciation to William H. Kruskal, Leonard J. Savage, and especially David L. Wallace of the Committee on Statistics at the University of Chicago for the care with which they read the manuscript, corrected technical errors and suggested other improvements, and referred me to numerous recent statistical sources which bear upon the subject matter of this book. I am likewise grateful to those persons and organizations that permitted me to make use of various materials as illustrative examples and tables. Acknowledgment is made throughout the text in connection with these materials.

Finally, I am indebted to the United States Public Health Service for its support of a research project entitled "Socialization, Personality and Mental Processes." The realization that the coefficient of intraclass correlation could be used effectively to summarize and describe many of the substantive findings of this research provided additional incentive to extend the logic and application of this method. This work was supported in part by research grant M-912 from The National Institute of Mental Health, of the National Institutes of Health, Public Health Service. Without this aid many aspects of the coefficient of intraclass correlation which are discussed in this book could not have been explored.

Chicago, Ill.   E.A.H.
January 1958

CONTENTS

list of tables   xv

glossary of symbols   xvii

I. introduction: history and logic of intraclass
   correlation   1

II. computation of the coefficient of intraclass correlation   10
   A. the case of equal class membership, 10
   B. the case of unequal class membership, 13

III. properties of the coefficient of intraclass correlation   17
   A. some properties of R, 17
      1. the limiting values of R · 2. the asymmetrical
      distribution of R · 3. the relation of R to F · 4. the
      statistical significance of R · 5. the confidence
      limits of R · 6. the relation of R_H to $\bar{r}$ · 7. the
      relation of R_C to $\bar{r}$

   B. some further comments on R and r, 29
      1. on the equality of the means and variances of
      the k-distributions · 2. on the indistinguishability
      of the within-class scores · 3. on the variance
      within classes and the problem of prediction ·
      4. on the relative accuracy of R and r

IV. introduction to the two-way classification   35

V. analysis of variance models and intraclass
   correlation   44
   A. introduction, 44

B. assumptions concerning properties of the data and their intended use, 46

C. the analysis of variance models, 50

    1. the one-way classification · 2. the two-way classification

D. some special cases involving two-way classifications, 62

    1. where the "finite population correction factor" (*fpc*) should be used · 2. where the $R'MS$ cannot be estimated from the data · 3. where $BCMS = 0$ when $K = \infty$ · 4. where an obtained R may be negative

VI. the application of intraclass correlation to reliability studies   73

    A. introduction, 73

    B. the use of r as an estimate of reliability, 76

    C. the use of R as an estimate of reliability, 79

    D. the estimation of reliability: a general case, 81

    E. the possible three-way factorial models, 93

VII. the application of intraclass correlation to pattern analytic studies   96

    A. introduction, 96

    B. definitions of profiles and patterns, 97

    C. the nature of the statistical problem, 99

    D. a proposed method for using R in pattern analytic studies, 102

        1. errors which are normally and independently distributed (uncorrelated) · 2. errors which are homogeneous from unit to unit

    E. application of the method to pattern analytic studies, 106

    F. illustration of the method with Wechsler-Bellevue data, 108

    G. illustration of the method with MMPI data, 112

    H. introduction to the problem of pattern analytic studies with groups, 118

VIII. the application of intraclass correlation to data in the form of ranks   123

    A. introduction, 123

B. some properties of intraclass correlation with ranks, 126
C. the computation of R_r, 129
D. the problem of tied ranks, 134
E. the statistical significance of R_r, 137
F. the relation of R_r and F_r to other methods for analyzing ranks in a $c \times k$ matrix, 139

appendix I   143

appendix II   149

    A.   Harris' Formula for R, 149
    B.   the relation of R_H to $\bar{r}$, 151
    C.   the relation of R_c to $\bar{r}$, 152
    D.   the relation of R_ϕ to R_c, 153
    E. R for the three-parameter case, 154
    F. R for the four-parameter case, 154

references   157

index   165

LIST OF TABLES

1. Achievement Scores of Random Samples of Students from Four Instructor Sections 12
2. Discrepancy Scores between Ability and Achievement for Members of Six High School Social Clubs 15
3. Measure of Hand Strength on Four Subjects, Five Trials Each 39
4. Summary of Expected Mean Squares and Proper Error Terms for Two-Way Classification Designs Assuming Randomness of Scores within Cells 56
5. Appropriate F's and R's for Various Two-Way Classifications under Assumptions Specified in Connection with Table 4 60
6. The Transformed Scores for Space Given to Twenty-Five Topics by Each of Five Textbooks in Educational Psychology 63
7. General Three-Way Analysis of Variance Model 86
8. Analysis of Wechsler-Bellevue Scores of Two Neurotics (N_1, N_2) 109
9. Illustrative Sample of R_P's Significant at the $\cdot 05$ and $\cdot 01$ Levels 110
10. Analysis of Wechsler-Bellevue Scores of Cases Designated Organic Brain Disease (O_1) and Adolescent Psychopath (P_1) Using Stabilized Scores 111
11. Analysis of MMPI Scores of a Single Individual over Five Trials (One Pre-shock, Four Post-shock Trials) Using Stabilized Scores 114

12. Summary of Findings for the Psychoneurotic and Psychotic Scales for the Four Post-shock Trials   117

13. Data in Table 6 Transformed into Ranks   131

14. Summary of Findings when Data in Table 3 are Transformed into Ranks   133

15. Individual Corrections for Tied Ranks   136

16. Values of F_r at the .05 and .01 Levels of Significance for Small Values of c Ranks and k Rankings   138

17. Values of R_r at the .05 and .01 Levels of Significance for Small Values of c Ranks and k Rankings   139

18. Interrelations among R_r, $\bar{\rho}$, W, η_r^2, χ_r^2, and F_r 140

19. Five Per Cent and One Per Cent Points for the Distribution of F 143

GLOSSARY OF SYMBOLS

SYMBOL	MEANING
∞	Infinity or very large number
$>, =, <$	Greater than, equal to, less than
$\geqslant, \leqslant$	Greater than or equal to, equal to or less than
$\doteq$	Is estimated by
$\sim$	$\sim$ over a symbol indicates a population value (e.g., $\tilde{R}$)
$\hat{}$	$\hat{}$ over a symbol indicates an unbiased estimate of a population value (e.g., $\hat{\sigma}_e^2$)
$^-$	$^-$ over a symbol indicates an average value (e.g., $\bar{k}, \bar{r}$)
$/$	Divided by (e.g., $SS/df = MS$)
SS	Sum of squares
TSS	Total sum of squares
MS	Mean square
$BCMS$	Between-classes mean square
WMS	Within-classes mean square, used in a one-way design
$BKMS$	Between-k's mean square in a two-way design
IMS	Interaction mean square when $s \geqslant 2$ in a two-way design
RMS	Residual or interaction mean square when $s = 1$ in a two-way design
$R'MS$	Residual mean square when $s \geqslant 2$ in a two-way design
C	Designation of the classification of classes
	Number of levels of the C classification in the population
	Correction term used in computing SS in Tables 1 and 2
c	Number of classes in the sample

SYMBOL	MEANING
K	Designation of the classification or number of members per class
	Number of levels of the K classification in the population
k	Number of members per class in the sample
$\bar{k}$	Average value of k (formula **4**, p. 14)
$\left.\begin{array}{l}I, J, K \\ i, j, k\end{array}\right\}$	Designation of classifications in the three-way design
S	Number of units or scores per cell in a finite population
s	Number of units or scores per cell in the sample
df	Degrees of freedom
e	Term for random, sampling, or otherwise uncontrolled errors
$E(MS)$	Expected mean square (in the probability sense)
fpc	Finite population correction
$\tilde{M}$	Population mean
n_1, n_2	df in numerator and denominator of variance (F) ratio
P	Level of statistical significance (e.g., P-value)
r_{tt}	Test-retest reliability coefficient (interclass)
sd_t	Standard deviation of a test or subtest
S-scores	Stabilized scores, where each subtest has the same variance over repetitions
σ^2	A component of variance (e.g., $\sigma_c{}^2$, $\sigma_{wc}{}^2$, $\sigma_k{}^2$, $\sigma_{ijk}{}^2$, $\sigma_e{}^2$)
$\tilde{T}$	"True" score, as on a test
V	Abbreviation for mean square in the three-way design
χ^2	Chi-square, a test statistic
r	Pearson's product-moment or interclass coefficient of correlation
$\bar{r}$	Average of k product-moment (interclass) r's
t	"Student's" test-statistic
	Symbol for the number of tied ranks in a set
z	Fisher's test-statistic
	Symbol used in connection with stabilized (S) scores
F	Snedecor's test-statistic (for its relation to R see formula **6**, p. 19)
F_{ck}	Test for significance of the $c \times k$ interaction in a two-way design when an error estimate is available (formula **19**, p. 105)

SYMBOL	MEANING
$F_k = F_L$	Test for significance of differences in k means or levels (formula **20**, p. 105)
F_p, F_o	F_p, the tabular value of F for a given P-value with the same df as an obtained F (i.e., F_o)
F_u, F_l	F's which correspond to the upper and lower confidence limits of an obtained F (cf. p. 23)
R	General coefficient of intraclass correlation (cf. formulas **2**, p. 11; **3**, p. 12; **5**, p. 14; **6**, p. 19)
R_H	R computed by Harris' formula or method (formulas **1**, **1'**, p. 10)
R_c	R corrected for presence of unequal k means or order effect in a two-way design (formula **8**, p. 38)
R_{ℓ}	R not corrected for the unequal k means or order effect in a two-way design
R_{ck}	A measure of profile dissimilarity (cf. R_P)
R_L	Intraclass correlation among k levels in a two-way design (formula **18**, p. 105)
R_P	A measure of profile similarity: $R_P = 1\text{-}R_{ck}$ (formula **17**, p. 105)
R_u, R_l	R's corresponding to upper and lower confidence limits of an obtained R (formula **7**, p. 23)
R_E	Coefficient of test unit equivalence (formula **9**, p. 87)
R_E^*	Coefficient of test equivalence: Spearman-Brown formula applied to R_E
R_S	Coefficient of test unit stability (formula **10**, p. 87)
R_S^*	Coefficient of test stability: Spearman-Brown formula applied to R_S
R_C	Coefficient of test unit consistency (formula **11**, p. 88)
$R_C^* = R_{K-R}$	Coefficient of test consistency: Spearman-Brown formula applied to R_C, which equals Kuder-Richardson formula 20 (formulas **13**, p. 89 and **15**, p. 92)
R_T	Coefficient of true test unit reliability (formula **12**, p. 88)

SYMBOL	MEANING
$R_T{}^*$	Coefficient of true test reliability: Spearman-Brown formula applied to R_T (formula **14**, p. 89)

Additional Symbols used in Connection with Ranks

TSS_r	Total sum of squares (formula **21**, p. 130)
$BCSS_r$	Between-classes sum of squares (formula **22**, p. 130)
WSS_r	Within-classes sum of squares (formula **23**, p. 130)
$BCMS_r$	Between-classes mean square
WMS_r	Within-classes mean square
C_t	Correction for tied ranks
ρ	Spearman's rank order coefficient of correlation
$\bar{\rho}$	Average of k rank order ρ's
W	Kendall and Smith's coefficient of concordance
$\eta_r{}^2$	Wallis' correlation ratio for ranks
$\chi_r{}^2$	Friedman's chi-square for ranks
F_r	F for data in the form of ranks (formula **24**, p. 130)
R_r	R for data in the form of ranks (formula **25**, p. 130)
$R_r{}^*$	Reliability of the mean of k sets of rankings (formulas **26** and **27**, p. 134)

I

introduction:
history and logic
of intraclass correlation

The processes involved in research usually require the investigator to perform a series of related tasks. These include the making of observations according to some design or under specified conditions, the recording of the observations, and the reduction of these data to provide summary statements appropriate to the phenomena under investigation. His summary statistical statements, which enable him to draw conclusions from his research data, often conform to one of two distinct but essentially related types: those pertaining to the probability of differences and those pertaining to the degree of consistency among scores or the relationship among variables.

As to the form of the statistics on which these statements are based, many of them are expressed as ratios of two variances or, more properly, of their best estimates. One of these is an estimate of controlled variation (or knowledge), and the other is of uncontrolled variation (or ignorance) with respect to the factors determining the data, the total variation being comprised of both. In research problems utilizing estimates of variance it is usually assumed that the total variation can be attributed in part to known causes (e.g., differences between experimental treatments or observed and hypothesized values) and in part to unknown causes (e.g., uncontrolled fluctuations or errors of sampling). In such research problems it is futile to apply statistical procedures when no controlled variation exists in the data, and it is redundant to do so when no uncontrolled variation is present.

It can be shown that many of the statistics designed to indicate whether the obtained differences reflect only random errors are, most simply, ratios of estimates of the sum of the controlled and uncontrolled variation divided by the uncontrolled variation to test whether the part attributable to controlled variation is greater than zero. The larger this ratio, the less likely it is that any observed differences are due to uncontrolled variation alone. Except for sampling errors, such variance ratios equal or exceed unity.

It can be shown also that many of the statistics designed to indicate the degree of relationship or association may be thought of as ratios of two variance estimates, namely, that of controlled variation (or covariation) to the total variation. The stronger the relationship, the larger the ratio will be. Because of their definition, these variance ratios may reach but they cannot exceed unity, since not more than all of the variation can be controlled or attributed to known causes.

It is thus apparent that the similarity of these two types of statistical statements is more fundamental than their apparent dissimilarity, which is due to the manner in which the two types of variance ratios are formed for their corresponding statistics.

The purposes of this book are to consider the history, logic, characteristics, and some important uses of the coefficient of intraclass correlation to estimate the degree of consistency or relationship among sets of scores, to relate this measure to various other statistics, to integrate the generalized correlation concept into the theory of analysis of variance models, and to show that the coefficient of intraclass correlation is a sufficiently general and powerful measure to recommend its use in the analysis of data from a wide variety of research situations in the social or behavioral sciences.

The coefficient of intraclass correlation (R) was developed in connection with the estimation of fraternal resemblance, as in the calculation of the correlation between the heights of brothers. If, in such cases, the sample is made up of pairs of brothers, one is not interested in the correlation between the taller and the shorter, or between the older and the younger, brothers, but rather in the correlation between the heights of brothers in general. In this example it is assumed that the two brothers are from the same parents, so that, if the heights of each pair are determined under homogeneous genetic conditions, such measures are logically interchangeable in computing the correlation coefficient.

In order to handle this type of problem, Pearson (1901) suggested the computation of a product-moment coefficient of correlation (r) from a symmetrical correlation table. According to this method, when two interchangeable scores are to be correlated, such as the heights of pairs of brothers, a double entry is made for each pair of scores in the correlation table. Thus, if one brother is 5′ 9″ and the other is 5′ 11″ tall, the entries $x = 5′ 9″$, $y = 5′ 11″$ *and* $x = 5′ 11″$, $y = 5′ 9″$ are made. The resulting distribution of scores is therefore symmetrical with respect to the diagonal of the table. When three or more scores exist in each class and are to be correlated in this manner, each possible pair of scores is entered in the symmetrical table. Following this procedure, it is also possible to compute a correlation when there is a varying number of entries in each class (e.g., brothers in a family). In computing r from a symmetrical table, one is in effect computing all possible correlations at once, and the computed r is the average of these correlations.

The number of entries in a symmetrical table rises very rapidly as the class membership increases. If each class (or family) has k members, $k(k-1)$ entries are necessary for each class in order to construct the symmetrical table. For example, when $k = 3$, $3 \times 2 = 6$ entries are required, but, when $k = 10$, $10 \times 9 = 90$ entries are required for each class. Consequently, although the computation of R from a symmetrical table is not difficult when k is small, it becomes exceedingly cumbersome when k is large.

To overcome this inconvenience Harris (1913) developed a short-cut method for obtaining the coefficient of intraclass correlation directly for classes of any size, thus obviating the need to construct a symmetrical table. But more important is his contribution to statistical theory, which lies in his discovery that the variance between class means can be separated from the total variance; that the coefficient of intraclass correlation can be defined as a ratio of two variances, the between-classes variance to the total variance; and that these variances can be estimated from two distributions, the distribution of class means and the distribution of the total set of observations.

As Harris observed, the concept of intraclass correlation is applicable to many problems in anthropology, sociology, and related fields. Harris called this measure "direct" intraclass correlation and also developed several special forms of this statistic, which he termed "cross," "inverse," and "fractional" intraclass correlations. (Boas, 1916, also recommended essentially the same approach, which he termed "fraternal correlation," for the treatment of certain anthropological data.) These statistics have been used very rarely by research workers in the behavioral sciences. One probable reason is that forty years ago these disciplines were not developed to the point where such techniques could be utilized. Another reason may be found in the particular path along which statistical and research methodology developed during this period, that is, with emphasis on methods and techniques designed to estimate the probability of differences among sample or class means, as in agricultural experimentation. In any case, intraclass correlation has remained almost in its initial form. It is ignored in many statistical texts and, where mentioned, the range of situations to which it is assumed to apply is usually restricted to the estimation of fraternal resemblance or to other cases where the scores in each class are interchangeable.

This is not to say, however, that intraclass correlation has been ignored by all research workers; it has, for example, been used in connection with research problems in agriculture (cf. Harris, 1913, 1914, 1915; Treloar, 1936; Fisher, 1950) and eugenics (cf. Fieller and Smith, 1951–52; Holt, 1952–53; Smith, 1952–53). But of more relevance to behavioral scientists is the work growing out of advances in design for experimentation and sample survey research. Because of their general importance, some of these applications of intraclass correlation will be mentioned briefly here.

The fact that the concept of consistency within classes can also be thought of as the nonindependence of scores within classes or samples immediately suggests the importance of intraclass correlation for the usual statistical analysis of data. This is particularly true for investigations in which t, F, or χ^2 is used as a test statistic. Since these statistics were developed on the assumption of the independence of measures in two or more samples, the presence of R would seem to distort the findings. In the case of t, for example, it is generally recognized that, when the observations are not independent, and the t-test based on the assumption of independence is used, the value of the obtained t will be overestimated if R is positive and underestimated if R is negative. Furthermore, the magnitude of the error is a function of the size of the intraclass correlation. It can be shown, for example, that, if t is based on 15 degrees of freedom (df) and is significant at the .05 level when randomness or independence obtains, the significance of the same t falls to the .135 level if the population correlation, $\tilde{R}$, is only .05, and to the .26 level if $\tilde{R} = .10$ (cf. Walsh, 1947). Similar effects exist when the F and the χ^2 tests are applied.

When correlation or nonindependence in this sense exists, R can be used to rectify the values of t, F, and χ^2. Similarly, if such techniques as cluster and stratified sampling are to be used properly, it is necessary to estimate the intraclass correlation in the population and to utilize R to obtain the appropriate standard errors (cf. Hansen et al., 1943, 1951, 1953; Marks, 1947; Cochran, 1953). However, a detailed consideration of the uses of R when nonindependence of observations may exist, as in experimentation or in survey sampling, is beyond the scope of our present discussion.

In the last few years psychologists and educators have shown a growing interest in intraclass correlation, but they have been concerned almost entirely with its use in obtaining estimates of test reliability (cf. Jackson, 1939; Jackson and Ferguson, 1941; Hoyt, 1941; Alexander, 1946, 1947; Brozek et al., 1948; Coombs, 1948; Ebel, 1951; Pilliner, 1952; Lindquist, 1953; Burt, 1955).

To understand the nature and uses of intraclass correlation it is first necessary to grasp the logic underlying this statistic, which pertains to the relative homogeneity of scores belonging to specified classes. A class may be defined as a set of elements which possess one or more common characteristics. In classifying scores one must be able to assign the scores unambiguously according to the definition of the classes. The coefficient of intraclass correlation is the measure of the relative homogeneity of the scores within the classes in relation to the total variation among all the scores in the table. Thus maximal positive correlation exists when all the intraclass scores are identical and the scores differ only from class to class. As the relative heterogeneity of the intraclass scores increases, the computed value of R will decrease; maximal negative correlation exists when the heterogeneity of the intraclass scores is maximal and all the class means are the same.

In more rigorous language, the coefficient of intraclass correlation may be phrased in terms of a ratio of components of variance which can be estimated directly from the usual analysis of variance table. It thus becomes clear that R will be related to the more familiar statistic, F. Even so, there are a number of important differences between F and R, two of which will be briefly mentioned here. In the first place, F is a test-statistic which may be used, for example, to test the possible "significance of difference" among a set of treatment means. And, because it is a test of significance, two or more F's are comparable only in terms of their corresponding P-values, unless they are specifically based on the same numbers of degrees of freedom. Other things equal, then, the size of F is a function of the number of degrees of freedom, and theoretically F has no upper limit. As a consequence F is not suitable as a general measure or index which has a relatively uniform meaning (Fisher, 1936). The coefficient R may be used as a general descriptive statistic whose maximal value is $+1$, and the magnitude of R is independent of the number of degrees of freedom upon which its estimation is based. Although the value of R tends to be uniform as a descriptive measure, its magnitude will be influenced by the size of k and by whether R is positive or negative. The exact limitations on its uniformity will be discussed in Chapter III—Properties 1 and 2 of R.

In the second place, and perhaps of greater importance, is the fact that F and R enable one to answer different questions: F *pertains to questions of difference; whereas R pertains to questions of similarity or agreement.* In many areas of research where the analysis of variance technique has been used extensively, it is of genuine importance to know whether different treatments yield different effects. In such cases, if the investigator has obtained a "significant" F, he is interested in the expected values of the subsample means as such. In agricultural research, for example, it is important to know the expected yield per acre from a specific type of seed and the extent to which it is likely to be superior to others that might be planted next year.

But not all of the questions that we may wish to ask of our data have to do with differences in this sense. In research involving attributes of persons, the relevant research questions often take the form of how much of the total variance of the measures randomly selected from various sources can be attributed to each source. More specifically, we may wish to know to what extent the variation of scores within classes (persons, traits, etc.) is less than the variation of scores between classes. Questions of this type may be approached by estimating the various sources or components of variation, and their relative magnitude, associated with each of the sources. In the discussions to follow, particularly with respect to questions of "reliability" and "pattern analysis," we shall be asking questions of this type and shall use R in finding answers to them.

The coefficient R is also related to the interclass or product-moment coefficient of correlation and to the average of any number of such coefficients ($\bar{r}$). Although certain arithmetic identities exist with respect to these coefficients under specific conditions, they are not logically identical measures. That both R and r are called measures of correlation rests in part on historical accident, since Pearson applied the term "correlation" to the coefficient computed from the symmetrical table. The use of the term correlation in connection with both R and r may be justified logically on the ground that each measure may be thought of as a ratio of two variances and the fact that, under certain conditions, they become equivalent algebraically. In the case of R, however, the numerator is an estimate of the variance among the class means, whereas the numerator of r

is an estimate of the covariance between the two variates. But, as Harris demonstrated, the variance of the class means can be shown to be arithmetically equivalent to the mean product-moment used to compute the numerator of r or $\bar{r}$ from a symmetrical table. In the case of both R and r, the denominator is an estimate of the average of the variance due to individuals without regard to any possible classification in terms of separate variates.

The congruence of R and r is most apparent when only two variates (e.g., x and y) are to be correlated, and when the means and variances of their distributions are identical in the sample. Utilizing these conditions, the basically different approach of R and r to questions of agreement or correlation can be illustrated by the following hypothetical examples:

Classes (e.g., persons)	Example A x, y	Sum	Example B x, y	Sum
a	1, 1	2	1, 5	6
b	2, 2	4	2, 4	6
c	3, 3	6	3, 3	6
d	4, 4	8	4, 2	6
e	5, 5	10	5, 1	6
Total	15, 15	30	15, 15	30
	$r = +1.00$		$r = -1.00$	
	$R = +1.00$		$R = -1.00$	

Although the computed values of R and r agree, the approach to their computation is different. The more familiar measure, r, is computed in Example A in terms of the x and y columns, and the identity of pairs of scores descending from 1,1 to 5,5 is apparent. Similarly in Example B, in going down the columns it is at once obvious that the pairs of scores are placed in reverse order.

In computing R, however, these data are viewed in terms of the scores along the rows or classes. Thus in Example A there is no variation between the scores in any of the rows from 1,1 to 5,5; rather all the variation is between the row sums (i.e., between the classes), namely 2, 4, . . ., 10. In Example B all the variation is within the rows or classes, with the result that there is no variation between class sums (i.e., each class sum equals 6).

There are, of course, other differences between R and r that would emerge if both measures could be applied to the same data.

These differences include the facts that R can be computed as readily when more than a pair of scores is involved, including cases where k varies from class to class, that R is sensitive to differences in the means and sigmas of the k distributions, and that the classes can be arranged along either a quantitative or a qualitative scale when R is used. These differences suggest that in certain respects R is a more general measure than r or $\bar{r}$. The fundamental difference between R and r rests, however, on the fact that R is a univariate statistic, whereas r is a bivariate statistic. That is to say, R is the appropriate measure of correlation when only one variate is involved, whereas r should be used when two variates (such as height and weight) are to be correlated.

From the fact that R is a univariate statistic it follows that this measure of correlation should be used in connection with the broad class of problems involving the estimation of the *reliability of measures*, since in reliability studies one is interested in determining the degree of similarity of scores, each of the same kind, from a number of individuals. The use of R to obtain estimates of reliability will be discussed in Chapter VI. Questions of *pattern analysis* are related to those of reliability in so far as one is interested in estimating the degree of intersubject agreement or intrasubject stability. Here, however, the problem involves the analysis of sets or profiles of scores, each of which is more or less different from the others in the set, but where each of the subscores to be compared is a measure of the same thing. The use of R in the analysis of such patterns of scores will be discussed in Chapter VII. Finally, the applicability of R to data in the form of *ranks* will be discussed in Chapter VIII.

II

computation of the coefficient of intraclass correlation

A. THE CASE OF EQUAL CLASS MEMBERSHIP

As we have seen, the coefficient of *intra*class correlation, R, was computed originally by calculating the coefficient of *inter*class correlation, r, after constructing what came to be called a symmetrical table. The actual computation of R was straightforward once such a table was prepared, but, because the preparation of a symmetrical table often proved to be tedious and time-consuming, Harris (1913) developed a formula which would estimate R as a simple function of two variances: (*i*) the variance of class means, and (*ii*) the variance of the total set of scores. Harris' formula may be written

$$1] \qquad k S_c^2 = S^2\{ 1 + (k + 1)R \}$$

where S^2 is the variance of the total set of scores, S_c^2 is the variance of the class means, and k is the number of members of each class. But formula 1 can also be written in terms of the mean squares of the analysis of variance table:

$$1'] \qquad \frac{BCMS^* - WMS}{BCMS^* + (k - 1)WMS} = R_H$$

where $BCMS$ is the between classes mean square, WMS is the within classes mean square from a one-way classification, where * on $BCMS$ denotes that it is a biased estimate of the population value, and where the subscript H denotes that R is obtained from Harris' formula (see Appendix IIA for proof and a definition of symbols in formulas 1 and 1').[1] The direction of the bias in R computed from a symmetrical table or by Harris' formula is always in the negative direction. The required correction for R in such cases is $\frac{1}{2} \log_e [c/(c - 1)]$ or, approximately, $+ [1/(2c - 1)]$, where c is the number of classes.

As early as 1908 "Student" had shown that, when unbiased estimates of population variances are to be obtained from samples, the proper divisor for the sum of squared deviations from the sample mean is one less than the number of cases in the sample. More specifically, unbiased estimates of the variances that enter into the computation of R may be obtained by using the mean squares of the analysis of variance table. Although the idea of estimating variances by using the number of degrees of freedom rather than the number of cases in the sample preceded Harris' discovery of formula 1 for computing R, it was left to Fisher to make use of this concept in all its generality. Thus it is to Fisher that we owe not only the refinement of the statistic R by correcting the bias which had heretofore been overlooked, but also the discovery that the unbiased estimate of the coefficient of intraclass correlation may be obtained in terms of the mean squares of the analysis of variance table. Utilizing Fisher's recommendation, the formula for estimating R may now be written

$$R = \frac{BCMS - WMS}{BCMS + (k - 1)WMS} \qquad [2$$

Formula 2 can also be expressed in terms of the expected mean squares, or $E(MS)$, for the population value of R (i.e., $\tilde{R}$).[2] The

---

[1] In formulas 1', 2 and 5 in this chapter, formula 6 in Chapter III, and formula 8 in Chapter IV, the $BCMS$, WMS, RMS and $R'MS$ are not precisely defined. Exact definitions of these terms will be given, however, in Chapter V.

[2] The $E(MS)$ mentioned here and in Tables 1 to 3 will be considered in more detail in Chapter V, along with exact definitions of R in various special cases, such as when R is negative. Formula 3 is based on the assumption that $K = \infty$ in the population; that is, one could continue indefinitely to add k members to c classes.

expected mean squares for $BCMS = \sigma_e^2 + k\sigma_c^2$ and for $WMS = \sigma_e^2$, where σ_c^2 and σ_e^2 are the estimated components of variance (see Chapter V). Substituting the $E(MS)$ in formula **2**, we have

$$3] \qquad \tilde{R} = \frac{\sigma_c^2}{\sigma_c^2 + \sigma_e^2}$$

Formula **3** is, in fact, a basic definition of intraclass correlation. In the discussion to follow, formula **2** or **3**, or refinements of them, will be used to provide the best estimate of $\tilde{R}$. Advantage will thus be taken of the direct relationship between intraclass correlation and the mean squares of the analysis of variance and, consequently, of the power and generality of the latter technique.

TABLE 1
Achievement Scores of Random Samples of Students from Four Instructor Sections

Classes	Scores of Pupils	Sum (x)	Sum (x^2)
a	54, 55, 51, 56, 53	269	14,487
b	56, 58, 50, 52, 60	276	15,304
c	63, 56, 62, 63, 61	305	18,639
d	51, 44, 48, 45, 46	234	10,982
		Total 1084	59,412

Computations

$$\text{Correction term } C = 1084^2/20 = 58,752.80$$
$$\text{Total } SS \ (19\ df) = 59,412 - 58,752.80 = 659.20$$
$$\text{Between-classes } SS \ (3\ df) = (269^2 + 276^2 + 305^2 + 234^2)/5 - C$$
$$= 296,318/5 - C = 59,263.60 - 58,752.80$$
$$= 510.80$$
$$\text{Within } SS \ (16\ df) = 148.40$$
$$BCMS = 510.80/3 = 170.27$$
$$WMS = 148.40/16 = 9.28$$
$$R = \frac{170.27 - 9.28}{170.27 + (5-1)(9.28)} = \frac{160.99}{207.39} = 0.78$$

Summary of Findings

Source of Variation	SS	df	MS	$E(MS)$†	R
Total	659.20	19			
Classes	510.80	3	170.27	$\sigma_e^2 + 5\sigma_c^2$	.78
Within	148.40	16	9.28	σ_e^2	

† $\hat{\sigma}_e^2 = 9.28$; $\hat{\sigma}_c^2 = 32.20$; $R = \hat{\sigma}_c^2 / (\hat{\sigma}_c^2 + \hat{\sigma}_e^2) = 32.20 / 41.48 = .78$. The ^ on σ^2 indicates that these estimates of components of variance are unbiased.

We can illustrate the main ideas of the foregoing discussion by an example. Let us take the data recorded in Table 1 which represent the achievement scores of random samples of five students from each of four instructor sections in a college mathematics course. Let us use these data to answer the question: "How can we characterize quantitatively the intrasection correlation, if any, in these data?" In this example the class sums are found to differ somewhat; this suggests the presence of intraclass correlation, but the above question can only be answered in terms of the relative variation of the class means to the total variation among all the scores. Specifically, *BCMS* (for variation among class means) is 170.27 for 3 *df*, *WMS* (for variation within classes) is 9.28 for 16 *df* and $k = 5$. By substituting these values in formula 2 we find that $R = .78$.

B. THE CASE OF UNEQUAL CLASS MEMBERSHIP

In the foregoing discussion it was assumed that the number of observations in each of the classes is constant. This was done merely to simplify the presentation both of treatment and of formulas. It is likewise possible to derive a suitable formula to compute R even if membership is not uniform over the classes. Situations involving unequal k's are not uncommon in practical work. This may happen, for example, whenever equal numbers of subjects for each class were not available for study in the first place, or whenever the data for some subjects were not recorded properly, or otherwise might be lost to the investigator.

It may be noted first that such a situation would raise no issue if we were willing to construct the symmetrical correlation table, compute R by Pearson's product-moment method, and make the proper correction for the bias in r (Fisher, 1950). This would only mean a different number of entries for each class and, in general, $k_i(k_i - 1)$ entries for the ith class with k_i members. The resulting table would still be symmetrical, and the product-moment correlation coefficient from this table would provide an estimate of the correlation. Obviously it would not be very efficient to adopt this procedure.

One could, of course, also compute R with unequal numbers

of class members by Harris' method but, as before, the value of R would be underestimated. Consequently it would be better to estimate the value of R in terms of the mean squares of the analysis of variance table. Since the situation is now analogous to the one-way analysis of variance table with unequal numbers for the various classes, the $BCMS$ and the WMS can be obtained as usual, but in order to compute R a suitable value of k is needed. The average (i.e., $\bar{k}$) is given by the formula

$$\textbf{4]} \qquad \bar{k} = \frac{1}{c-1}\left(\sum k_i - \frac{\sum k_i^2}{\sum k_i}\right)$$

where c is the number of classes, k_i is the number of members in the ith class, and $\sum$ stands for summation over all classes. With this approximation, the formula for computing R is essentially the same as formula **2** with $\bar{k}$ substituted for k. Thus we may write

$$\textbf{5]} \qquad R = \frac{BCMS - WMS}{BCMS + (\bar{k}-1)WMS}$$

To illustrate the computation of R when membership varies from class to class, we may analyze the set of data collected by Davis, Hess, and Fielder, which is given in Table 2.[3] In a study of 61 high school seniors who were members of six "nonofficial" social clubs, marked consistencies were observed in the social behavior patterns of the members within each club and marked differences between clubs. In addition, standardized measures of the intellectual ability, performance in academic school subjects, and indices of the discrepancy between these two measures were collected for each of the club members. Three boys' and three girls' clubs were studied; membership varied from 3 to 13 seniors in each club.

With reference to this example one may ask, "In relation to their ability, to what extent is their academic achievement correlated with

[3] I am grateful to Dr. Allison Davis, Dr. Robert D. Hess, and Miss Marie Fielder for permission to cite the data used in this example. These data were collected as part of a project on personality and cultural factors in problem solving under the direction of Davis and Hess; the data cited here were collected and analyzed by Miss Fielder. See: Fielder, M. The school as a social system: A study of the social organization of a high school senior class. Ph.D. dissertation in progress, University of Chicago.

TABLE 2

Discrepancy Scores between Ability and Achievement for Members of Six High School Social Clubs

Club	Discrepancy Scores of Club Members	Sum (x)	Sum (x^2)	k_i	k_i^2
1	28, 32, 23, 34, 28, 30, 28, 30, 31, 30, 30, 29, 40	393	12,063	13	169
2	7, 24, 17, 16, 28, 29, 33, 21, 16, 20, 15, 25	251	5,831	12	144
3	34, 37, 37, 25, 30, 23, 29, 35, 38, 33	321	10,547	10	100
4	25, 23, 33, 38, 18, 21, 16, 29, 23, 26, 22, 16, 22	312	7,978	13	169
5	27, 26, 15, 18, 7, 31, 26, 33, 15, 25	223	5,579	10	100
6	1, 10, 19	30	462	3	9
	Total	1530	42,460	61	691

(x) = raw discrepancy score + 25

Computations

$$\text{Correction } C = (1530)^2/61 = 38,375.41$$
$$\text{Total } SS \ (60 \ df) = 42,460 - C = 4084.59$$
$$\text{Between-clubs } SS \ (5 \ df) = (393^2/13) + (251^2/12) + (321^2/10) + (312^2/13) +$$
$$(223^2/10) + (30^2/3) - C$$
$$= 40,195.78 - C = 1820.37$$
$$\text{Residual } SS \ (55 \ df) = 4084.59 - 1820.37 = 2264.22$$
$$k = \left(\frac{1}{5}\right)\left(61 - \frac{691}{61}\right) = 9.93$$
$$BCMS = 1820.37/5 = 364.07$$
$$WMS = 2264.22/55 = 41.17$$
$$R = \frac{364.07 - 41.17}{364.07 + (9.93 - 1)(41.17)} = .44$$

Summary of Findings

Source of Variation	SS	df	MS	$E(MS)$†	R
Total	4084.59	60			
Classes (clubs)	1820.37	5	364.07	$\sigma_e^2 + 9.93\sigma_c^2$	.44
Within	2264.22	55	41.17	σ_e^2	

† $\hat{\sigma}_e^2 = 41.17$; $\hat{\sigma}_c^2 = 322.90/9.93 = 32.52$; $R = \hat{\sigma}_c^2 \ / \ (\hat{\sigma}_c^2 + \hat{\sigma}_e^2) = 32.52 \ / \ (32.52 + 41.17) = 32.52/73.69 = .44$.

their social behavior patterns as indicated by club membership?" To answer this question, R was computed from the discrepancy between the standardized ability and achievement scores of the 61 seniors. Table 2 shows that, in this example,

$$\sum k_i = 61 \quad \sum k_i^2 = 691$$

and, by formula **4**,

$$k = \left(\frac{1}{5}\right)\left(61 - \frac{691}{61}\right) = 9.93$$

The value of the *BCMS* (for variation between club means) is 364.07, and the *WMS* (for variation within clubs) is 41.17. By using formula 5 the value of *R* is found to be .44. Thus we may say that a relationship between club membership and the extent to which these children utilize their intellectual potential in terms of academic achievement is characterized by an intraclass correlation coefficient of .44.

III

properties of the coefficient of intraclass correlation

Traditionally the use of intraclass correlation has been restricted to cases analogous to the one-way analysis of variance model. The two examples given in the last chapter are typical in this respect. The conditions under which R may be estimated in cases analogous to the two-way or more complex analysis of variance models will be discussed in later chapters. The present chapter will consider certain important properties of R which are generally applicable.

A. SOME PROPERTIES OF R

1. the limiting values of R

An obtained R may take a value between $+1$ and $-1/(k-1)$, where k is the number of members in each class. Since by formula **2**

$$R = \frac{BCMS - WMS}{BCMS + (k-1)WMS}$$

it is obvious that, in general, R is positive when $BCMS > WMS$ and is negative when $BCMS < WMS$, the magnitude of a negative R

depending in part on the value of k. R will attain its maximum value when the WMS is minimal. Since the WMS cannot be negative, its minimum value is zero. Substituting zero for WMS, the formula for R reduces to $(BCMS/BCMS)$, which equals $+1$. This is the maximum value that R can take. The upper limit of R is thus independent of k, the class membership. This is as should be expected: if there is perfect positive intraclass correlation, the scores within each class must be identical (i.e., only the class sums will differ), and it should not matter how many scores are in each class.

The above formula also shows that R will attain its minimum value when the $BCMS$ is minimal. Since the $BCMS$ cannot be negative, its minimum value is zero, and, if we substitute zero for $BCMS$, the formula for R reduces to $-1/(k-1)$. This is the minimum value (in the algebraic sense) that R can take. Since k is always positive, the lower limit of R decreases as k increases. Thus, unlike the maximum positive value of R, which is independent of k, the minimum value of R depends only on k. In particular, when $k = 2$, the minimum value of R is -1, and when $K = \infty$, the minimum value of R is 0. (For a more explicit discussion of negative R's, see sections 2 and 4 below and Chapter V, Special Case 4.)

2. the asymmetrical distribution of R

As seen from property 1, the lower limit of R depends on the size of k, whereas the upper limit is $+1$ regardless of what k may be. This introduces asymmetry in the distribution of R, the extent of which depends on the value of k. Furthermore, this dependence becomes more and more apparent as k increases, making the distribution of R progressively skewed, with the result that a negative value of R does not have the same significance (as a departure from independence) as the arithmetically equivalent positive value. Caution is therefore necessary in the interpretation of the coefficient of intraclass correlation, especially when R is negative and when $k>2$.

The asymmetrical distribution of the correlation coefficient when $k>2$ should not, however, be identified with R alone. The interclass correlation coefficient, r, which may be used only when $k = 2$, shows the same degree of asymmetry, and for the same reasons, when the average of $k(k-1)/2$ r's is computed when $k>2$. Thus, if $\bar{r}$ is interpreted as a measure of the over-all agreement among k distributions, the minimal value of $\bar{r}$ is $-1/(k-1)$, so that, when $k>2$ and the k distributions disagree maximally, $\bar{r}$ will be $-1/(k-1)$ rather than -1.00. This is not a limitation of either R or $\bar{r}$ but is a consequence of the fact that, when more than two distributions are involved, complete disagreement among all of them is not possible. For example, if there are three judges and two of them disagree, the third cannot disagree completely with both of the other judges.

3. the relation of R to F

If we divide both the numerator and the denominator of formula 2 by WMS, we get

$$R = \frac{F-1}{F+(k-1)} \qquad [6$$

and, conversely,

$$F = \frac{1+(k-1)R}{1-R}$$

which shows that R and F are functionally related. This relationship is monotonic; that is, R and F increase or decrease together. This may be shown simply by partially differentiating R with respect to F (or F with respect to R), which gives

$$\frac{\partial R}{\partial F} = \frac{(F+k-1)-(F-1)}{(F+k-1)^2} = \frac{k}{(F+k-1)^2}$$

which is always positive, and hence the relationship is monotonic.

4. the statistical significance of R

The level of significance of R is identical with that of the corresponding F (i.e., $BCMS/WMS$). In other words, the hypothesis that an observed R could have come from a population with zero $\tilde{R}$ can be tested by the F-ratio computed from the same mean squares, with the appropriate df, as were used to obtain R.

That this identity in terms of the levels of significance of R and F should obtain can be shown in various ways. Intuitively, by virtue of Property 3, R and F increase or decrease together, so that for any high (or low) value of R the corresponding F will also have a high (or low) value; and, if the latter is significant, the former is also. Formally, however, the significance of R can be determined by transforming R to the z scale by the relation

$$z = \tfrac{1}{2} \log_e \frac{1 + (k - 1)R}{1 - R}$$

Then the level of significance of R will be the same as that of z (Fisher, 1950). But we have already seen that

$$\frac{1 + (k - 1)R}{1 - R} = F$$

and therefore $z = \tfrac{1}{2} \log_e F$. Thus z may be obtained by taking half the natural logarithm of the F-ratio and then referring to Fisher's table of z. But, since Snedecor (1956) has tabulated the value of F corresponding to many values of z, the transformation to z is unnecessary. Consequently the level of significance of R can be obtained directly from the tables of F.

The .05 and .01 per cent points for the distribution of F are given in Table 19, Appendix I.[1] In this table n_1 refers to the number of df in the numerator of F (i.e., the larger mean square) and n_2 to the number of df in the denominator of F (i.e., the smaller mean square). When R is positive, as it is in the majority of cases, the F will be defined as: $BCMS/WMS$, with n_1 the df for $BCMS$ and n_2 the df for WMS. The term ".01 point" or "1 per cent point" refers to the point on the F-scale beyond which 1 per cent of the F-distribution lies (for a given number of df for n_1 and n_2). The size of this area is usually referred to as the "P-value" or "level of significance."

---

[1] More extensive listings of F-values are given in Merrington and Thompson (1943); Hald (1952b); Lindquist (1953); McNemar (1955); Pearson and Hartley (1956); and Snedecor (1956).

The procedure for determining the statistical significance of an obtained R may be illustrated by reference to the data in Tables 1 and 2. In Table 1 the F corresponding to the R of .78 may be obtained by the ratio $BCMS/WMS = 170.27/9.28$, which equals 18.35 for 3 and 16 df. The value in the F-table for $P = .01$ for 3 and 16 df is 5.29; consequently this F of 18.35, and hence the corresponding R of .78, are "significant" at less than the .01 level. Similarly the F corresponding to the R of .44 in Table 2 is obtained by the ratio $BCMS/WMS = 346.07/41.17 = 8.84 = F$ for 5 and 55 df. This value of F exceeds 3.37, which is the F corresponding to $P = .01$ for 5 and 55 df. In subsequent tables the appropriate P-value corresponding to the obtained R will be given.

The F-table, however, is generally appropriate only for the one-tail test required in the analysis of variance; that is, only the probability values that $BCMS > WMS$ are given. When $BCMS > WMS$, $F > 1$ and R is positive. Thus, since the F-table corresponds to $F \geqslant 1$, only positive values of R can be tested directly for significance. When the $BCMS < WMS$, which results in a negative R, the significance of the R corresponds to that of the reciprocal of the F which is > 1 with the df interchanged. Or, following the rule that the ratio (larger mean square/smaller mean square) is distributed as F, the ratio $WMS/BCMS$ may be computed and the customary F-table entered with the df corresponding to the WMS and $BCMS$. Kendall (1952, p. 361) gives the sampling distribution of R for a normal population and equal numbers of members within classes, and Bhargava (1946) has given a method for testing the significance of R for classes of unequal size. For practical purposes, however, the question of the significance of R can be answered in terms of the significance of the F-statistic as outlined above.

In using the F-table to determine the significance of a meaningful negative R it should be remembered that both ratios, $BCMS > WMS$ and $BCMS < WMS$, could occur equally often by chance alone. However, in connection with the more familiar analysis of variance table in which F is used to test hypotheses regarding differences between treatment or sample means, the investigator is interested only in the case where $BCMS > WMS$ (i.e., the one-tail test). In testing the significance of negative R's, we are also using a one-tail test (i.e., the other tail of the F-distribution). Whenever the investigator is able to predict (correctly) ahead of time whether the obtained R will be positive or negative, the above method for testing the significance of R should be used. However, whenever the investigator is not able to make such a prediction, the P-value obtained by the above method should be doubled, since the two-tail test should be used under these conditions.

Whereas the minimal value of an obtained R will depend on the size of k in the *sample*, the interpretation of an obtained negative R will depend on the size of this value in the *population*, which will be designated by the symbol K. Thus, regardless of the size of an obtained negative R, one would not expect it to be less than $-1/(K-1)$, where K refers to the population value. If, for example, $K = \infty$ in the population from which the sample is drawn, an obtained R of less than zero would have no meaning other than not being greater than zero, since, if k were increased by additional sampling, one would expect the obtained negative R to approach zero. If an obtained negative R exceeds the theoretical lower limit of $-1/(K-1)$, the discrepancy is due, presumably, to sampling errors.

If, however, the class membership is defined as being limited to a specified small size, R can take a negative value and be interpreted meaningfully. An example of such limited class size occurs when $K = 2$ in the case of "friendship pairs." If the classes are composed in terms of traits on which the members complement each other, one would expect that, if one member is scored high, the other member would be scored low, as in Example B in Chapter I. In such cases, if "opposites attract each other," one should expect to obtain a negative R and could interpret it meaningfully. Repeated sampling would increase the number of classes, but not the size of K (see also Chapter V, Special Case 4).

5. the confidence limits of R

The confidence limits of R define the interval which is expected to include $\tilde{R}$, the population value, a given per cent of the time if a large number of samples are taken. It should be noted, however, that the confidence interval does not imply that $\tilde{R}$ varies, or that $\tilde{R}$ actually lies within this interval on the basis of data from any particular sample.

The size of the confidence interval will be determined by F_o (the F corresponding to the obtained R) and F_p (the table value of F corresponding to a given P-value with the same df as F_o). The table value of F corresponding to $P = .01$ will give the 98 per cent, and the F corresponding to $P = .05$ will give the 90 per cent limits, and so on. The 98 per cent confidence interval will be broader than one of 90 per cent for the same obtained R. (For tables of F necessary to obtain other than the 90 and 98 per cent confidence limits, see footnote, page 20.)

The confidence limits of R can be derived from Fisher's derivation of the confidence limits for his z distribution (Fisher, 1950). After one has decided upon a specific confidence interval, such as the 90 per cent interval, the confidence limits of an obtained R can be estimated most easily by substituting in formula 6 the F-values which correspond to the upper and lower limits of that interval. The F's which correspond to the specified upper and lower limits of R are obtained as follows: $F_u = F_o \times F_p$, and $F_l = F_o/F_p$, so that the

$$\text{Upper confidence limit} = R_u = \frac{F_u - 1}{F_u + (k - 1)}$$

and the   [7

$$\text{Lower confidence limit} = R_l = \frac{F_l - 1}{F_l + (k - 1)}$$

In Table 1, for example, $R = .78$ and the F_o for 3 and 16 df equals 18.35. To obtain the 90 per cent confidence limits for this R, we find the F which corresponds to $P = .05$ for 3 and 16 df in Table 19, Appendix I. The appropriate $F_p = 3.24$. Consequently, for the above R of .78, the corresponding

$$F_u = 18.35 \times 3.24 = 59.45$$

and $$F_l = 18.35/3.24 = 5.66$$

Substituting the values of F_u and F_l in formula **7**, we have

$$R_u = \frac{59.45 - 1}{59.45 + 5 - 1} = .92$$

and

$$R_l = \frac{5.66 - 1}{5.66 + 5 - 1} = .48$$

Similarly, for Table 2, the 90 per cent confidence limits for the R of .44 are computed by multiplying the F_o of 8.84 by the F_p of 2.38 to obtain F_u and dividing 8.84 by 2.38 to obtain F_l. In this example $\bar{k} = 9.93$. Using $\bar{k}$ instead of k and substituting these values in formula **7** we have

$$R_u = \frac{21.04 - 1}{21.04 + 9.93 - 1} = .67$$

and

$$R_l = \frac{3.71 - 1}{3.71 + 9.93 - 1} = .21$$

By the same method the 98 per cent confidence limits for the R of .78 in Table 1 are $R_u = .95$ and $R_l = .33$, and the 98 per cent confidence limits for the R of .44 in Table 2 are $R_u = .74$ and $R_l = .14$. For consistency and simplicity of presentation, only the 90 per cent limits will be given for R's computed in subsequent tables.

For some time it has been clear that, in problems of estimation, the confidence limits of a statistic yield information which, in many respects, is of greater practical utility than the P-value. In this connection it should be recalled that the size of the P-value of a test statistic is partly a function of the number of cases (or, more properly, the df's involved in its estimation), so that, even though a result is of negligible significance from a practical point of view, a "statistically significant" P-value often can be secured by adding enough additional cases. It follows that exclusive emphasis on the P-value may obscure the fact that frequently if a difference, trend, or relationship is worth discussing at all, its presence should be evident with a moderate number of cases.

With reference to the statistic R, overemphasis on its P-value may be misleading. Suppose, for example, that the R computed in Table 1 had been an estimate of "reliability." This R of .78 is highly significant in a statistical sense ($F_o = 18.35$; $F_{.001} = 9.00$), but the lower limit for the 90 per cent confidence interval, R_l for 3 and 16 *df*, is only .48. In the context of a reliability study it may be of little reassurance to know that one can be highly confident that, on the basis of the obtained R of .78, the value of $\tilde{R}$ is not zero (which is all that the *P*-value tells us), when the chances are 1/20 that $\tilde{R}$ may be as low as .48. However, on the assumption that events which did occur are the ones which are most likely to occur (cf. Kendall, 1949), the obtained R of .78 is still the best estimate of $\tilde{R}$.

The number of observations on which a statistic is based will, of course, influence the size of the confidence interval for that statistic. However, an increase in the number of observations on which an R is based will decrease the size of its confidence interval. Such information is in no way misleading, but rather increases the precision with which one can make statements pertaining to the probable size of the correlation in the population. It is in this sense that the confidence interval is often spoken of as denoting the precision of an estimate.

Finally, knowledge of the confidence interval may be used to determine whether two R's could have been drawn from the same population or, in other words, whether they differ significantly. We have seen, for example, that the lower confidence limits for the two R's in Tables 1 and 2 are both positive values. This is another way of saying that they are "significantly greater than zero." If two obtained R's are to be compared, one can observe whether they fall within each other's specified confidence intervals. If they differ widely with respect to their confidence intervals, they may be said to differ at that specified level of significance.

To test whether two R's differ in borderline cases it is possible to determine the significance of the difference between two independently obtained coefficients of intraclass correlation, R_1 and R_2, by means of the relation between R and Fisher's z statistic (cf. Fisher, 1950). Since

$$z = \tfrac{1}{2} \log_e \frac{1 + (k - 1)R}{1 - R}$$

which is distributed approximately normally with variance

$$\sigma_z{}^2 = \frac{k}{2(c-2)(k-1)}$$

Where c, the number of classes, is sufficiently large,[2] we may test the significance of the difference between two obtained R's as follows: If the obtained R's are independent, the distribution of the difference between their corresponding z-values (i.e., $z_1 - z_2$) is approximately normal with variance

$$\sigma_{z_1 - z_2}{}^2 = \frac{k_1}{2(c_1 - 2)(k_1 - 1)} + \frac{k_2}{2(c_2 - 2)(k_2 - 1)}$$

where c_1 and k_1 correspond to these values for R_1, and c_2 and k_2 correspond to these values for R_2.

Since the distribution of the difference between two z's is approximately normal, the table for the normal deviate, or the normal curve, may be used to determine the approximate P-value for the significance of the difference between two independent R's. For example, if the ratio $(z_1 - z_2)/(\sigma_{z_1} - z_2)$ yields an absolute difference which is greater than 2, we would consider that R_1 and R_2 differ at the .05 level of significance. (Jellinek, 1940, has also suggested that this procedure can be used to test the difference between two F-ratios and in comparing the relative heterogeneity of two samples of data.)

6. the relation of R_H to $\bar{r}$

The remainder of this chapter will deal with data arranged in the form of a two-way classification (or "two-fold table," or "two-dimensional design," or "two-factor experiment"). Although the logic and rationale for intraclass correlation when this design is involved is discussed more fully in Chapters IV and V, it is considered here because of certain properties of R and the fact that when this design is involved it is possible to make explicit certain relations

---

[2] The lower limit of c for which this test may be used is not determined. In connection with r, however, Hald (1952a, p. 609) points out its appropriateness "even for small values" of c. And, since R is more accurate than r, and since the variance of z is uniform, it seems safe to assume that c, the number of classes, can be as small as 5.

between R and $\bar{r}$ when both measures can be applied to the same data.

In the examples discussed in Tables 1 and 2, we have been looking at the scores primarily along one direction only—the direction corresponding to the scores between the rows or classes. However, if the scores are arranged in a $c \times k$ matrix[3] and if the intraclass correlation is high, it will be apparent that in any row, a high (or low) score is likely to be followed by a high (or low) score as we move along the row. Looking next at the pairs of columns, that is, vertically along columns instead of horizontally along rows, if the above conditions obtain it is to be expected that the $k(k - 1)/2$ intercolumn product-moment correlation coefficients (r's) will be high and consequently their mean ($\bar{r}$) will be high also. Similarly, if R is low, scores in any row are not consistently high or low, but they vary widely. Under these conditions the $k(k - 1)/2$ intercolumn r's will tend to be low, as will be their mean. This suggests that R and $\bar{r}$ may be related.

Under certain conditions to be specified, the mean intercolumn correlation coefficient ($\bar{r}$), obtained by averaging via Fisher's z transformation, is exactly equal to R_H computed from the set of ck observations. Therefore, in order to get the mean of the $k(k - 1)/2$ intercolumn correlations, when its use is warranted otherwise, it is enough simply to compute R. The exact conditions under which the above result obtains are as follows.

If the k scores within each of the c classes are distinguishable, so that the ck observations can be arranged in a $c \times k$ matrix with c rows and k columns, the arithmetic mean of all the $k(k - 1)/2$ intercolumn r's is exactly equal to the R_H computed from all the ck observations. That is to say, $R_H = \bar{r}$, provided that: (i) the means of the k column distributions are equal arithmetically; (ii) the variances of the k column distributions are equal arithmetically; and (iii) the R is computed by Harris' method (see Appendix IIB for proof).

As observed before, the value of R_H computed by formula 1

---

[3] The symbols C and K refer, in general, to the two classifications whenever the two-way model is being considered. The symbols C and K refer to specific classifications in the *population* or designate the number of levels in them; the symbols c and k refer to specific classifications in the *sample* or designate the number of levels in them. A different set of symbols will be used in connection with discussions of the three-way model in Chapter VI.

or **1′** is slightly biased. This result also shows incidentally that $\bar{r}$ computed by averaging $k(k-1)/2$ separate r's through the z transformation, besides involving much more computational work, is likewise biased—unless the bias in each r is corrected before averaging. This bias may be considerable if c, the number of classes, is small.

7. the relation of R_c to $\bar{r}$

If the k scores within each of the c classes are distinguishable so that the ck observations can be arranged in a $c \times k$ matrix with c rows and k columns, and there exists a known, but irrelevant, factor to which the differences among the successive column means can be assigned and should therefore be partialed out, the arithmetic mean of all the $k(k-1)/2$ intercolumn r's is exactly equal to R computed from all the ck observations, provided that: (*i*) the unequal means of the k column distributions are equalized with a loss of $k-1$ degrees of freedom; (*ii*) the variances of the k column distributions are equal arithmetically; and (*iii*) the R is computed by using formula **8** (see Appendix IIC for proof). Note that in this case R_c, and therefore the estimate of $\bar{r}$, is unbiased; hence an unbiased estimate of $\bar{r}$ may be obtained directly by computing R_c (see also Chapter IV for a discussion of R_c, the R computed after any differences among the k means is removed).

The above identities of R_H and $\bar{r}$, and R_c and an unbiased estimate of $\bar{r}$, should not be interpreted to mean that R and r are identical measures. Their essential differences lies in the fact that R is a univariate statistic whereas r is a bivariate statistic. The utility of the relationships specified above lies in the fact that, when $\bar{r}$ is desired, it is usually easier and less time-consuming to equalize the k column means and variances and compute R than it is to compute the $k(k-1)/2$ separate r's, correct for the bias in each r, and then average them through z to obtain $\bar{r}$.

In spite of the practical usefulness of the relation R_H or $R_c = \bar{r}$ under certain specified conditions, the situations where this relationship obtains are still the idealized cases in which the specified conditions must hold strictly. Since these conditions are seldom met in practice and some departures from the ideal will be observed as a rule, it is pertinent to investigate how such departures will affect the above relationship.

The first condition refers to the equality of the k column means, whether observed or achieved through statistical procedures. The effect of eliminating the observed differences among the k column means is a function of the magnitude of these differences. In general, the equalization of the means will tend to increase the value of R unless the variation among the k column means is equal to or less than that due to the error factor only. As shown in the next chapter, the effect of equalizing the k means can be determined by comparing the $BKMS$ with the RMS (the residual or "interaction" mean square in a $c \times k$ matrix with one score per cell).

The second condition refers to the equality of the variances of the k column distributions. When the variances do differ, the simplest procedure is to equalize them arithmetically by dividing each score in a column by the standard deviation of that column. Then the variances of the k column distributions will be equalized and this condition of Properties 6 and 7 will be satisfied. If the means and variances of the k column distributions are equalized in order to compute R as an efficient and quick estimate of $\bar{r}$, the effect is to reduce the statistic R to r or $\bar{r}$. This and related points will be discussed in the following section.

B. SOME FURTHER COMMENTS ON R AND r

1. on the equality of the means and variances of the k-distributions

We are now in a position to examine more closely certain similarities and differences between R and r. But to do this requires a brief statement regarding what r is, essentially, and what it does. The bivariate coefficient of interclass correlation (r) measures the relationship between pairs of scores on two different, definite, and defined variates, such as height and weight. But, since the two different variates do not have the same units of measurement, it is first necessary to convert the raw data into standard scores (of zero mean and unit standard deviation) which are then independent of the original units of measurement. Stated otherwise, the means and the variances of the two distributions to be correlated are equalized either before or while computing r. As a consequence r is not sensitive to any differences which may be observed between the k means and variances in the raw data, and, if this information is of any importance, it is thrown away when r is computed.

But what if, on some a priori ground, the means and/or the variances of the two distributions are expected not to differ? Any observed differences may then reflect the presence of extraneous or uncontrolled factors which should be examined and/or accounted for, rather than automatically removed and hence ignored by using standardized scores to equalize the means and variances. The fact that important information in the data may be discarded when r is computed has frequently caused statisticians and research workers to become disenchanted with its use (cf. Tukey, 1951). The statistic R, on the other hand, is sensitive to differences between the means and/or the variances of the k-distributions, and, as these differences increase, the magnitude of R decreases.

2. on the indistinguishability of the within-class scores

We have seen that r should be used when a measure of correlation is desired in cases where two different scales are involved, whereas R should be used when the scores within a class are of the same kind. If the scores are not of the same kind, standardization is required and r is in order. These considerations indicate that R and r should not be used interchangeably.[4] In Chapter I we have also noted the logical dissimilarity in the manner in which R and r approach the

---

[4] It happens all too frequently, however, that r, owing to its general familiarity, has been employed inadvertently where R would have been the appropriate measure. Examples of such inadvertence are common, especially for the case of $k = 2$, perhaps because that is the only case where r may be used. The use of r instead of R will be discussed in more detail in connection with the estimation of "reliability."

question of agreement or correlation. There are other differences between R and r, including the limitation of r which gave rise to initial computation of the correlation from a symmetrical table.

It will be recalled that R was first used in connection with the estimation of fraternal resemblance from physical characteristics, the usual example being the correlation of heights of brothers. If the problem is to estimate the correlation between two brothers in terms of their height, one has no criterion for assigning one brother to the x-distribution and the other to the y-distribution. If one did use such a criterion, the resulting correlation (r) would not answer the question raised above; rather it would answer a question such as "What is the correlation between the taller and shorter, or older and younger, brothers?" Pearson suggested that the question of correlation among brothers in general could be answered by using the method of multiple entries to construct the symmetrical table. It was from this use of R that the concept of indistinguishability of scores within classes arose.

In many types of data the scores within classes are in fact logically indistinguishable, and in such cases R is the proper method of estimating the correlation. The following illustration with sociometric data will indicate how R may be used to answer such questions as the extent to which children who choose each other as "best friend" may resemble one another in terms of other known characteristics.[5] More specifically, a group of approximately 75 boys and 75 girls were asked to name their best friend at least once a year over a period of 7 years. In addition, a large number of other measures were also obtained on each child every 6 months during this period, and they included a variety of physical, personality, mental, and social variables. Using mutual mentions (e.g., Bill chose Ted and Ted chose Bill) to define pairs (or classes) of children, the question may be answered by computing R for the pairs of children on such

---

[5] I am grateful to Drs. Harold E. Jones and Mary C. Jones, University of California, Berkeley, who provided the data for this example from the California Growth Study (Jones, 1939a, b). Similar examples of the use of R with $K = 2$ are found in Newman *et al.* (1937), and Snedecor (1956, p. 283) gives an analysis of one set of data from this study of twins.

variables as I.Q. or physical maturity. As one example, R was computed on the I.Q. scores (in standard score units) on a group of 18 friendship pairs made up of 11-year-old boys, and was found to be .23. The *BCMS* is based on the variation between pairs, and the *WMS* is based on the variation within pairs; this example differs from Table 1 in that $k = 2$ instead of 5.

It is possible that the degree of resemblance between the friendship pairs thus defined will change over a period of time. The same procedure would be followed in computing R on subsequent mutual choice groupings. If the size and composition of such groupings vary with time, and the degree of relationship between variables changes with age, it is to be expected that such changes will be reflected in the value of R (cf. Jones, 1948).

If an attempt had been made to compute r from these data, some procedure for assigning members of each pair to the x- and y-distributions would be required. But, as we have noted above, to use such a procedure would have precluded an answer to the research question. Furthermore, the practice of assigning the members "at random" involves considerable risk, since the r estimated by this method might be substantially in error. To indicate the range of possible r's with the data just cited, in one case the boy with the higher I.Q. was always assigned to the x-distribution, and in another case the boy with the higher I.Q. was assigned to the x- and y-distributions alternately. The first r was .69 and the second r was .20. The fact that R is the appropriate measure of correlation when indistinguishability of scores within classes exists is of importance in many types of psychological and sociological research where "intact groups" such as clinical syndromes, social classes, or other pre-formed groups are used.

3. on the variance within classes and the problem of prediction

One of the chief uses of the coefficient of interclass correlation has been to answer the following general question: "Given an r and a new value of x, what is the value of y expected to be?" If the regression of y on x is linear, a value of y can be estimated for any new value of x with accuracy specified by the "standard error of estimate" if the *true regression line* is known (cf. Anderson and Bancroft, 1952, Ch. 13; Wallis and Roberts, 1956, Sec. 17.3). Such estimation is possible and can be made with known precision if the variance of the x's is uniform and the y's are normally distributed about the true regression line.

If one is interested in predicting in an analogous sense with R, the parallel case exists when the variances within each class are the same and the class means are equally spaced. In the case of R, however, the above question would be phrased in a slightly different form, such as: "Given an estimate of the variance within classes, and knowing the class means, to which class should a new score be assigned and with what confidence?"

In the case of r, the higher the correlation (or the smaller the variance of the y's around the true regression line), the greater will be the accuracy in predicting a given y score. Similarly, with respect to R, the higher the correlation (or the smaller the variance within classes), the greater will be the accuracy in allocating a given score to its proper class, provided the means of the classes are equally spaced. In the case of R, the estimate of the variance within classes is the WMS; consequently the $\sqrt{WMS}$ can be used with R in the same manner as the "standard error of estimate" is used with r.

In making such comparisons, however, one should keep in mind that R, a univariate measure, is not strictly comparable to r, a bivariate measure. Furthermore, in the case of R, the arrangement of the classes need not be equally spaced along a quantitative linear scale; in fact, they are frequently defined in terms of some qualitative classification and may be arranged in any order. In Table 2, for example, the class means from a to f are: 30.2, 20.9, 32.1, 24.0, 22.3, and 10.0. For a given WMS, however, R will reach a maximum value when the class means are equally spaced. The latter condition permits maximal differentiation among the class means, which results in a maximal $BCMS$ for a given WMS (see Property 1 of R).

If the $\sqrt{WMS}$ is used to predict class membership, it must be assumed that the within-class variances are the same from class to class; that is, they should not differ significantly. But this assumption applies generally to the use of the analysis of variance technique, and hence to R. In practice, however, the class variances may differ, in which case the meaning of the P-value and the confidence limits of an R computed from such data are open to question. If the class variances differ significantly and are related to the size of the class means, certain adjustments (such as an appropriate transformation of the raw data) are in order to equalize the within-class variances. Or, if classes with excessive variances can be removed from the table, R will be increased, since the variation within each class contributes to the WMS, and as the WMS is reduced the R will be increased. But, in any case, inspection of the class variances, which are easily computed, provides the investigator with an important source of information regarding his data (see discussion of Table 3). However, if one is interested in predicting class membership, various multivariate methods exist which are more appropriate for this purpose.

4. on the relative accuracy of R and $\bar{r}$

When R and $\bar{r}$ may be applied to the same data, R will always be the more accurate estimate of the population value, $\tilde{R}$, except when the latter is $+1$. The difference in accuracy of the two estimates will vary as k and $\tilde{R}$ vary. When $k = 2$, R is based on $2c$ observations, whereas r is based on the c independent pairs of observations. When k exceeds 2 and $\tilde{R}$ is in the neighborhood of 0, the accuracy of R is equivalent to $\frac{1}{2}k(k - 1)c$ independent pairs of observations, which gives R a very substantial advantage in accuracy over $\bar{r}$ when k is large. As $\tilde{R}$ increases, the relative advantage of R over $\bar{r}$ decreases, so that when $\tilde{R}$ is in the neighborhood of $+.50$ the accuracy of R is equivalent to approximately $9c/2$ independent pairs of observations used to compute $\bar{r}$ (cf. Fisher, 1950). Consequently, in addition to its greater convenience and generality, R will generally yield an estimate of the population correlation which is substantially more accurate than $\bar{r}$, especially when k is large.

IV

introduction to the
two-way classification

Except for the last part of Chapter III, we have thus far considered the case where the scores within the classes are not distinguishable, so that the order in which they are entered in a class is of no importance. In Table 1, for example, we could have entered the five scores in class a in any order, and similarly for the five scores in the other classes, and the value of R would not have been affected. This is the principle of "indistinguishability" which, some writers have assumed, is a necessary restriction on the use of R. Or, in other words, it has been held that R can only be used in connection with designs analogous to the one-way analysis of variance model. This has been a rather severe restriction, and its acceptance has precluded the effective use of R in summarizing data from a wide variety of research situations.

Incidentally, it will be recalled that the early work on intraclass correlation was concerned with the estimation of fraternal resemblance, such as the heights of brothers. One might infer that this work was done using data from adult subjects; otherwise the frequent confusion concerning "indistinguishability" of scores within classes would have been removed long ago. If, for example, the research problem had dealt with the correlation of heights of brothers within a family from early adolescence to maturity, with measurements taken on each birthday, it would have been obvious that the factor of age (or growth) would have been relevant to the question being asked. Assuming indistinguishability in this example, the R would have been negative because the variation in the scores of each brother due to his increased height from year to year (WMS) would have been greater than the variation between the brothers ($BCMS$). But, if the effect of the age factor were removed and if the brothers kept their same relative position with respect to height, we would expect R to be positive.

It often happens that the scores within each class are distinguishable and therefore may be presented meaningfully according to some order implicit in the phenomenon under observation as, for example, when the first score in one class corresponds to the first score in all the other classes, and so on. In such cases it is possible that an *order effect* exists.[1] If in this sense a meaningful order is inherent in the data, the importance of being able to remove its effect (a trend or other differences among the k means) applies immediately to a great deal of the research conducted in the behavioral sciences. For example, when measurements relate to psychological variables and are taken on the same individual over intervals of time, the experiences which intervene the trials, the changes which these experiences produce within the individual, and the effects which these intraindividual changes have on his scores cannot be overlooked if one is to analyze his data efficiently or completely. In other words, if one set of scores provided by the same subject is considered along the time axis, and if there are factors to which the improvement or deterioration on successive trials may be attributed (and which may be irrelevant to the research question), this fact should be recognized and the effect of

---

[1] The term *order* need not imply an ordinal scale, but rather that variation exists among the means of the k-distributions. The idea of removing such sources of variation before computing R is not new. For example, Harris (1914) observed that, when intraclass variability is due in part to systematic or known causes, which could legitimately be removed but are allowed to remain, R will be in error. Specifically, if the proper correction is not made, the RMS will be overestimated and R will be underestimated. Similarly Mather (1943) suggested that under certain conditions a complete analysis of the data is possible in computing R and that this is one of the essential differences between R and r.

such factors removed before the data are examined for relative consistency within the classes. Such situations are often met in reliability
studies when factors such as learning, memory, practice, forgetting,
fatigue or other conditions are involved in determining the size of
the scores. A design based on the presence of an order effect (the
distinguishability of the k-distributions) is also used whenever R and
r or $\bar{r}$ may be computed from the same data, and provides the
basis for comparisons between R and the coefficient of interclass
correlation.

If an order effect which exists in the data could be dealt with
properly, it would not be necessary to require the scores within a
class to be indistinguishable initially. In fact, to achieve indistinguishability *de facto* in such cases, it is essential that the order effect,
as expressed in differences in the k means, first be removed. *If* one can
legitimately assume that there is no "interaction" between the classes
and the columns, the order effect can be removed without difficulty
by equalizing the means of the column (or k) distributions which are
identifiable. There are various methods of doing this. We could subtract from each score the mean of the column in which it lies. A more
useful method would be to partial out the differences among the
column means in the analysis of variance. Although both procedures
involve a loss of $k - 1$ df for equalizing the k means, the latter has an
obvious advantage over the former, namely, that, if one removes the
sums of squares due to the k mean differences, it is possible to apply
the F-test to determine the statistical significance of the difference
between the column means. If any differences among the k means can
be partialed out in the analysis, the concept of intraclass correlation
is extended so that the two-way analysis of variance model can be
utilized.

Procedurally, the problem becomes analogous to a $c \times k$ analysis
of variance table with one score per cell. The total variation is now
attributable to three sources: (*i*) class means; (*ii*) column means or
order effect; and (*iii*) residual, which is assumed to be intraindividual
variation and measurement error. The corresponding degrees of
freedom are $(c - 1)$, $(k - 1)$, and $(c - 1)(k - 1)$. The mean squares
may be denoted $BCMS$, $BKMS$, and RMS, where RMS indicates

that the within classes residual mean square is free from the order effect. The formula for R may then be written

8]
$$R_c = \frac{BCMS - RMS}{BCMS + (k - 1)RMS}$$

where the subscript c of R denotes that the correction due to differences in k means has been applied.

As for the influence of the order effect on R, the value of the intraclass correlation coefficient corrected for differences in k column means exceeds, equals, or is less than the value of the uncorrected coefficient, according as the variation between the k column means arithmetically exceeds, equals, or is less than that due to random errors. Symbolically,

$$R_c \gtreqqless R_f \quad \text{according as} \quad F_k \gtreqqless 1$$

where R_c = the coefficient of intraclass correlation corrected for differences in the k column means in a two-way table, R_f = the coefficient of intraclass correlation not corrected for differences in the k column means, and

$$F_k = \frac{BKMS}{RMS}$$

(see Appendix IID for proof).

The finding given above relates the effects of the magnitude of R to the partialing out of the differences in the k column means. There is also the consideration of the significance of the R obtained when the differences in the k column means are partialed out at the loss of $k - 1$ degrees of freedom. The F corresponding to the $BCMS/RMS$ will then be based on $(c - 1)$ and $(c - 1)(k - 1)$ df instead of on $(c - 1)$ and $c(k - 1)$ df, and the loss in the number of df may sometimes be enough to change a significant R_f into a nonsignificant R_c, although the latter is slightly higher than the former. This effect on the level of statistical significance may occur, for example, when c and k are small, and when the difference between the k means is slight.

Certain considerations involved in removing the order effect can be illustrated by analyzing a set of "reliability" data provided by

Wissler (1901, p. 38).[2] In this example, which is given in Table 3, five successive ergometer readings (measuring hand strength) were taken on each of four subjects. Although the data in this table appear to be similar to those in Table 1, in that $c = 4$ and $k = 5$, the difference is that in Table 3 the classes are defined in terms of individual subjects, and each subject contributed five successive scores. This being

TABLE 3

Measure of Hand Strength on Four Subjects, Five Trials Each

Classes (Subjects)	k Trials					Sum (x)	Sum (x^2)	Estimate of Within-Subject Variance
	1	2	3	4	5			
a	45	40	43	42	40	210	8,838	4.50
b	100	80	70	70	60	380	29,800	230.00
c	70	65	75	65	67	342	23,464	17.80
d	70	55	40	35	40	240	12,350	207.50
Sum (x)	285	240	228	212	207	1172		
Sum (x^2)	21,825	15,250	13,974	12,114	11,289		74,452	

Summary of Findings

Source of Variation	SS	df	MS	E(MS)†	R	F	P	90 per cent Confidence Limits
Data Analyzed in Terms of One-Way Classification								
Total	5772.80	19						
Subjects ($c = 4$)	3933.60	3	1311.20	$\sigma_{wc}^2 + 5\sigma_c^2$	(.68)	?	?	?
Within	1839.20	16	114.95	σ_{wc}^2				
Data Analyzed in Terms of Two-Way Classification								
Subjects ($c = 4$)	3933.60	3	1311.20	$\sigma_{ck}^2 + 5\sigma_c^2$	.77	18.13	.01	.46–.93
Trials ($k = 5$)	971.30	4	242.83	$\sigma_{ck}^2 + 4\sigma_k^2$	.37	3.36	.05	
Residual	867.90	12	72.33	σ_{ck}^2				

† For the data analyzed in terms of the one-way classification: $\hat{\sigma}_{wc}^2 = 114.95$; $\hat{\sigma}_c^2 = 239.25$; $R = \hat{\sigma}_c^2 / (\hat{\sigma}_c^2 + \hat{\sigma}_{wc}^2) = .68$.
For the data analyzed in terms of the two-way classification: $\hat{\sigma}_{ck}^2 = 72.33$; $\hat{\sigma}_c^2 = 247.77$; $\hat{\sigma}_k^2 = 42.63$; $\hat{\sigma}_k^2 + \hat{\sigma}_{ck}^2 = \hat{\sigma}_{wc}^2 = 42.63 + 72.33 = 114.96$.

[2] I am grateful to the American Psychological Association for permission to cite Wissler's data.

the case, we might expect to find a degree of within-person consistency (or "correlation") among the within-class scores. Let us assume that we are interested in the extent of the within-person consistency over these five trials.

From a casual examination of the data in Table 3 it is apparent that we can view it either in terms of (*i*) the scores of these four subjects on five trials or (*ii*) some general statement regarding the performance of subjects over trials on ergometer readings. In the former case, if there are marked differences among the subjects in their responses over the trials, we cannot make one general statement about all of them but will have to consider the subjects separately or group them in some manner and talk about the behavior of the subgroups separately. Or, in more technical terms, if an "interaction" exists between subjects and trials, we cannot make an inclusive statement which accurately describes all four subjects. If, however, we are interested in making general statements regarding the effects of trials on this task, we are not interested in the performance of single individuals, but rather would assume that any inconsistencies, as indicated by a subject-trial interaction, are typical and hence must be taken into account in making such general statements. (Technically, the difference between *i* and *ii* above are described by the terms "fixed" and "random" analysis of variance models. A more complete discussion of such models will be given in Chapter V.)

For the time being let us assume that we wish to analyze the data in Table 3 in terms of the performance of the four subjects on the five trials. In order to analyze these data it is necessary to obtain an appropriate estimate of the RMS. Possible confusion in computing this value may arise because, by arranging these data in a $c \times k$ matrix, we have only one score per cell and no opportunity to compute an estimate of the residual or "error" variance based on within-cell variability. If we can legitimately assume that there is no interaction between subjects and trials, that is, if the trial effects are the same from subject to subject, the fact that we have only one score per cell offers no difficulty. If no interaction in this sense exists, we can subtract the sums of squares attributable to the trial (or order) effect from the within-subjects (i.e., within-classes) sums of squares to obtain the RMS.

The assumption of no interaction frequently is of questionable validity in the case of such psychological data, and in the present example this assumption appears to be untenable to say the least. This is apparent in the results shown in Table 3, where it is seen that the estimated within-subjects variances are: 4.5, 230.0, 17.8, and 207.5. The wide discrepancy among these values might be interpreted to mean merely that the subjects vary widely in their variability on this task. But, because of the trend shown by subjects b and d, the difference among the above variances clearly indicates that the trial effects are not the same from subject to subject. Rather, as Wissler observed, it is evident that subjects a and c showed much less fatigue over the five trials than did subjects b and d.

Suppose in this case that we subtract the sums of squares (SS) for trials (971.3) from the within subjects SS in the one-way table (1839.2) to obtain a new residual SS (867.9) from which to compute the RMS. If we do so, we know that this value contains both the desired residual based on within-subject variability *and* any inter-action effect, and furthermore that the latter two sources of variation cannot be separated. Knowing that the interaction is not zero, we are forced to qualify any general statements regarding the interpretation of the order effect and the R in this case.

Specifically, we find from Table 3 that the $BKMS/RMS$ as here defined is 3.36 for 4 and 12 df, which falls at about the .05 level of significance. Or, stated differently, regardless of the fact that the RMS is overestimated (because the interaction effect is confounded with it), a general trial effect is still found to exist over the four subjects. As for the computed value of R, we find that it rises from .68 to .77 when the trial effect is removed. But, because the RMS is overestimated in this case, the R of .77 is to some extent lower than it would be if we could also partial out the interaction effect. As the strength of the interaction effect increases, R will decrease, so that in extreme cases the computed value of R may be negative. We can, however, gain some idea of where R might fall if the interaction were zero. This can be done by grouping subjects a and c and b and d and then computing separate R's. Doing this, we find that, for subjects a and c, $R_c = .98$ and, for subjects b and d, the corresponding

$R_c = .85$. Furthermore, the former R rises from .97 to .98 and the latter R rises from .61 to .85 when the order effect is removed, indicating that for the latter pair the order effect is more pronounced. This finding checks with the fact that the within-classes sums of squares for subjects a and c are much smaller than for subjects b and d, as seen in Table 3. These differences are also reflected in their corresponding F's for the trial or order effect, which are 2.78 and 6.13 respectively.

We may also wish to approach Table 3 in terms of the relative consistency of the scores within the k columns. Again assuming that the persons $\times$ trials interaction is zero, R and F can be estimated by means of the $BKMS$ and the RMS, with the result that the between columns $R = .37$ $(P = .05)$. Because interaction is known to exist in these data, however, this finding indicates the existence of considerable consistency among the means of the five trials, since R and F are underestimated in this case.

When the data can be properly arranged in a two-way classification, there should be no difficulty in computing the proper estimate of R when two or more scores are present in each cell (with an equal number of scores in each cell). If the data in Table 3 had been in this form, we could have used the variation within cells to estimate the two R's, and also could have isolated the interaction effect and tested the significance of the class, order, and interaction effects. The within-cell scores should be independent measures, preferably obtained on separate occasions.

In conclusion, it should be noted that the above discussion regarding the analysis of the data in Table 3 holds only if we are interested in the performance of these four subjects on the five (k) trials and wish to confine our conclusion to these subjects and trials. On the basis of this formulation of the problem, we must either be able to assume that no interaction exists, or obtain a measure of random variation based on the within-cell variation in order to compute R and F. If, however, we are interested in making inferences about the effect of trials in general, and assume that the five trials and four subjects are samples drawn at random from much larger populations, the interaction term should be used to estimate

R and F regardless of whether one or more scores exist in each cell.

It is thus clear that *the proper approach to the analysis of a given set of data depends on a variety of assumptions that one makes (explicitly or implicitly) about the data, experimental design, and the particular analysis of variance model employed.* These matters will be discussed in some detail in the next chapter.

V

analysis of
variance models and
intraclass correlation

A. INTRODUCTION

In the preceding chapters we have seen that R possesses a variety of properties and characteristics which recommend it as a useful measure of the relative homogeneity or consistency among sets of scores or, if one wishes, of the relationship among sets of variables. We have also seen the essential relation of R to the analysis of variance and the F-test of significance, and that R can be computed directly from the mean squares of the analysis of variance table. But, in connection with the example given in Table 3, we have also seen that *in approaching specific data the analysis of which appears to be simple and straightforward, mere computational ease does not provide a guide for appropriate description or inference.*

Even though the analysis of variance may have grown out of Harris' discovery that the sums of squares can be partitioned into independent portions, it is necessary at the present time to examine certain recent developments in the theory and technique of the analysis of variance in order to understand the principles by which one can compute meaningful estimates of R and F from samples of empirical data. This is particularly true when the two-way (or more elaborate) classifications are used. This chapter will deal with the essential aspects of the pertinent two-way analysis of variance models and their theoretical and procedural implication for computing appropriate intraclass correlations.

The technique known as the "analysis of variance" is an elegant arithmetic or computational device which is based on a set of algebraic identities, and as such has no inherent relation to events or phenomena in the real world. If this device is used properly, however, it provides a highly efficient method for analyzing empirical data from many types of research situations in order to describe various aspects of the real world. The proper use of this device requires some understanding of its properties, which understanding enables one to follow certain rules in carrying out the analysis of data.

The importance of such rules can be illustrated by recalling the necessity of following specified procedures in connection with other devices which are less elaborate than the analysis of variance models. Suppose, for example, that we wish to count a collection of objects on a table. Our use of the familiar numerical system requires us to assign one numeral to each object, in the order: 1, 2, 3, . . ., n, until all the objects have been designated by a separate natural number, with no numbers omitted as we count. If we are to count "correctly" the number of objects, it is necessary to follow such specified rules. A somewhat more complicated device is the calculating machine. We may use this device to add, divide, or perform a variety of other operations. But in each case it is necessary to follow certain specific rules, such as entering the figures in the specified order with the decimal points in the same position on the keyboard if we are adding a series of numbers.

It is true, of course, that one can disregard the rules in using such devices and still obtain an "answer"; but, if the rules are ignored, we say that the answer provided by the device is false (or meaningless) in the sense that it does not pertain to "reality." Unfortunately, none of the devices of the type we are considering here can force us to use the appropriate rules or tell us whether the rules actually were followed, so that we cannot evaluate the meaningfulness of the "answer" by mere inspection of it. Rather, it is up to the investigator to know and follow the rules appropriate to the device that he is using.

Some of the rules appropriate for the proper use of the analysis of variance technique are usually expressed in the form of the "assumptions" which underlie its use. However, the analysis of variance models, even more than the calculating machine, may be used for a variety of different purposes, which may vary in complexity and kind. Some of the more important rules associated with the use of the analysis of variance technique, and hence of R, will now be considered.

B. ASSUMPTIONS CONCERNING PROPERTIES OF THE DATA AND ITS INTENDED USE

In the analysis of any particular set of data the assumptions which apply require that the data be in a form congruent with certain basic properties of this device and with its intended use. For example, the investigator may wish merely to describe certain aspects of a particular set of data. In order to make use of the analysis of variance as an efficient computational device, it must be assumed that the data are in a form such that (*i*) the various controlled and uncontrolled sources of variation are additive, (*ii*) the random errors must be uncorrelated and also (*iii*) should have the same variance. In practice, the data may not fully meet these assumptions, but at least they should be approximated if the analysis of variance technique is expected to provide unbiased minimum variance estimates of the effects of the controlled sources of variation. Incidentally, no assumptions regarding the characteristics of the population are thus far involved, so that, if assumptions (*i*) to (*iii*) regarding the data are met, R may be computed as a descriptive measure.

In the majority of cases, however, the investigator does not wish merely to describe the findings of his experiment, but rather is interested in generalizing his findings beyond his obtained data. That is to say, he wishes to make inferences about certain characteristics (called parameters) of some hypothetical or real, finite or infinite population on the basis of his findings derived from a sample drawn at random from that population. If he wishes to make valid inferences, an additional assumption is required, namely, that (*iv*) the random components and errors should be normally distributed in addition to being uncorrelated among themselves and having a common variance. The assumptions regarding the distribution of the trait or characteristic in the population (such as normality) are required *only if* statistical inferences are to be made regarding the population parameters. If assumption (*iv*) is also met, inferences can be made regarding the statistical significance and confidence limits of R.[1]

The probability that assumption (*ii*) will be met or approximated is increased by selecting the *experimental units* at random from the population of such units being sampled. The concept of the experimental unit is fundamental to the theory underlying the analysis of variance, since the estimate of random errors is properly based on the variation of independent units within cells or CK classifications. Thus the units are those entities to which the levels of the C and K classifications are assigned at random, and they refer to that aspect or attribute of persons, objects, places, or events which is *measured as a unit* and recorded in the cells of the analysis of variance design. In any particular case the unit may be the score for an individual, one of a series of scores for an individual, one of a series of trials, and so on.

The distinction is frequently made between two types of statistical inference: (*i*) *tests of significance* to answer questions regarding the interrelations among a set of sample *means* or, more specifically, whether one can infer that two or more sample means differ significantly, and (*ii*) the *estimation of population parameters*. After obtaining an estimate of the population mean(s) and/or variance(s), one is faced with the question of its reliability or stability. To answer this question it is necessary to analyze the data in terms of those aspects which are concerned with its variability. This type of statistical inference involves the identification of the separate sources of variability

---

[1] These assumptions are discussed in detail in many statistical articles (cf. Eisenhart, 1947) and textbooks (cf. Anderson and Bancroft, 1952). See also references in Haggard (1949).

and estimation of their magnitude; the *components of variance* are thus estimates of the variation from various sources that, acting in concert, make up the total variance of a given score or experimental unit.

Although most research workers are more familiar with the use of the analysis of variance technique to test the significance of the differences among a set of means, the estimation of the components of variance is a more general and fundamental approach to the analysis of data. When two or more sources of variation are known to affect the data, the magnitude of each of the components of variance can be estimated for each of the identifiable sources of variation as well as for the source of variation due to random errors. To put the matter differently, the analysis of the total variance into its component parts provides a general approach to data analysis, and the components of variance can be used for rather different purposes —one of which is to make tests of significance. It is only by an appreciation of the nature of the components of variance and the possible relations among them that one is able to determine the appropriate significance tests for the variety of particular experimental designs. We shall return to this point later in the chapter.

The relative and absolute magnitudes of the components of variance, and functional relations among them, are used in various ways in connection with problems of statistical inference. One of these uses is in the estimation of the accuracy of a population mean. Thus in certain situations the investigator may wish to obtain an unbiased estimate of the general mean and to determine its confidence limits. In an example given by Eisenhart (1947) the objective was "to determine very precisely *the* body temperature" characteristic of a given species of animal. Here the temperature of a sample of animals taken at random from the species was recorded on a sample of days taken at random. In this case there is no interest in possible differences among the temperature readings of individual animals or days. Rather, the factors of animals and days are used to estimate the components of random variation associated with each in order to obtain an unbiased estimate of the confidence limits of the mean temperature for the species. In experiments involving two or more subsample means the investigator may also wish to estimate the confidence limits of one or more specific subsample means. Thus in both these cases estimates of the absolute magnitude of appropriate components of variance are obtained in order to estimate the scalar range within which the population mean(s) may be expected to fall.[2]

The investigator may also be interested in the relative magnitude of the components of variance. In industrial research, for example, he may wish to know which of several sources of variation contribute most to the variability of the final product in order to know how to raise the quality level of that product. Or, an educator interested in preparing class materials for the effective teaching of a given subject matter may wish to determine whether pupil achievement is influenced more by differences among teachers or among methods of teaching. Knowledge of the components of variance associated with each source provides information which may be used to improve the presentation of such materials. The estimation of components of variance can, of course, enable one to analyze effectively data from many other types of research situations. For example, in the study of perceptual processes the investigator may wish to sample a variety of stimulus situations, stimulus objects and subjects, and to isolate the effects of each of the sources of variation and their interactions (cf. Brunswik, 1956). Estimates of the components of variance may be used also in a variety of other important ways, such as planning future experiments (cf. Anderson and Bancroft, 1952, Chs. 22–25) or increasing the efficiency of testing schedules (cf. Lindquist, 1953, Ch. 16).

Our primary interest here, however, lies in the fact that the estimate of the coefficient of intraclass correlation may be defined as a ratio of components of variance (cf. formula 3). If one wishes to compute R's in connection with experimental designs more complex

---

[2] When the absolute magnitude of the components of variance is involved, it may be desirable to estimate their confidence intervals. The problems involved in estimating the variances and confidence intervals of the components of variance are not solved, although approximate solutions are available (e.g., Satterthwaite, 1941). These approximations are summarized in Anderson and Bancroft (1952, Ch. 22), and Harter and Lum (1955, pp. 22–26).

than the traditional one-way classification, it is necessary first to understand the concept of components of variance and the method of estimating them. Furthermore, since the corresponding F is used to estimate the significance and confidence limits of R, it is essential that the proper numerator and denominator be used in computing F in a variety of two-way classifications. And, because the proper residual (and certain other) mean squares differ depending on the particular experimental design, it is necessary to make explicit which mean squares should be used in computing R and F in each case.

C. THE ANALYSIS OF VARIANCE MODELS

Before considering the details of computing the R's and F's obtained from the analysis of data from one-way and two-way classifications of data, we shall first examine briefly the nature of the classification. Up to now we have spoken only of the "classes" and the "order effect." During the remainder of this discussion it will be more convenient to generalize the term classification to designate the variates which are sampled in a particular experimental design. Thus we shall have c levels or conditions of classes (C) and k levels or conditions of order (K) with s scores in each cell. In designating the C and K classifications, we shall continue to use C, K, and S to refer to the population values for the classifications and c, k, and s to refer to the levels of C, K, and S in the sample. Each classification will then have two or more levels, and the number of scores in each cell will be one or more, with a constant number in each cell. (The problems involved in obtaining maximum likelihood estimates when s varies from cell to cell are quite complicated—if unbiased solutions are possible at all—and beyond the scope of this discussion.)

In designating c levels of C and k levels of K in any experimental design it is essential to make explicit in connection with each classification (i) whether the levels used in the design exhaust all the possible levels in the population, (ii) whether the levels are taken at random from an infinite (or very large) number of levels in the population, or (iii) whether the levels are taken at random from a finite (and relatively small) number of possible levels in the population. In case (*i*) we say that the classification is *fixed*, in (*ii*) it is *random*, and in (*iii*) it is *random from a finite population*.

These three types of classification may be illustrated by the six social clubs in Table 2. If there are only six clubs and we have studied all of them, or if we wish to describe these six clubs and do not wish to make any statements regarding clubs in general, we consider this classification *fixed*. If, however, we consider that these six clubs are taken as a random sample from a very large population of social clubs, and wish to make generalizations about the larger population of such clubs, we consider this classification *random from an infinite population*. Finally, if we assume that there are, say, only fifteen clubs and we have sampled at random six of them, and if we wish to generalize our findings to the fifteen clubs, we consider this classification *random from a finite population*. (Incidentally, in connection with Property 4 of *R* in Chapter III, we saw that a knowledge of whether *K* is fixed or random in the population is necessary to interpret the meaning of an obtained negative *R*. Similarly in Chapter IV we saw that in the analysis of the data in Table 3 it is first necessary to determine whether the two classifications are considered fixed or random.)

It will be apparent that, if in a two-way classification both *C* and *K* are of type (*i*), we have what is called a *fixed model* or "Type I Model"; that, if both are of type (*ii*), we have a *random model* or "Type II Model"; and that if one classification is of type (*i*) and the other is of type (*ii*), we have a *mixed model* analysis of variance design. First we shall consider the fixed, random, and mixed models, and later an illustration in which a classification of type (*iii*) is involved. Finally, it will also be seen that *the selection of the proper error or residual term necessary to compute R and F will depend on which one of the possible analysis of variance models are employed in any particular experimental design*.

It should be noted, however, that it is not always possible to assume that the levels of a given classification are fixed, random, or random from a finite population. Rather, it frequently occurs that the investigator selects *arbitrarily* a small number of levels from a very large number of possible levels of some classification. Such instances occur, for example, when the investigator selects arbitrarily (and for good reasons) the following levels: 10, 32, 100, 316, and 1000 cycles per second in an auditory experiment, or 5, 10, 20, and 40 trials, or 8, 12, and 24 hours of food deprivation in an animal learning experiment. In such cases the particular levels are not selected at random, nor do they exhaust the many possible levels of the classification (e.g., cycles per second or time) being sampled. No model has been developed to deal with this type of situation explicitly, and some disagreement exists among statistical theorists regarding the nature of the model that should be used in analyzing the data obtained under such conditions. Correspondingly, confusion might arise in the mind of the investigator since it is sometimes possible to argue that the fixed, the random, or neither model is appropriate for analyzing a set of experimental data when the levels are arbitrarily selected.

In most cases the investigator can decide which of the above-mentioned models to use in terms of his research purposes and the extent to which he wishes to make generalizations from his data. If he is interested only in the arbitrarily selected levels and is willing to confine his conclusions to those levels, he should consider the classification fixed. (But few investigators are really interested in doing this.) Frequently, if the classification is a continuum or similarly meaningful function, the experiment may be thought of as a problem involving regression analysis (e.g., Anderson and Bancroft, 1952, p. 153ff.). From this point of view, the estimated value of some dependent variate (e.g., pitch or learned responses) is estimated on the basis of fixed variates (e.g., levels of cycles per second or time). In such experiments the classification involving fixed variates should, of course, be considered fixed. In other situations, which may be less clear, the investigator may wish to use the random model, since it will yield results which tend to be somewhat more conservative (see Tables 4, 5, and 7).

1. the one-way classification

On the basis that assumptions (*i*) to (*iv*), which underlie the use of the analysis technique are met (or approximated), we can assume that the definable sources of variation can be expressed in terms of a linear model. In the one-way classification, then, we can assume that the magnitude of any particular score (x) is a linear function of the over-all mean for the population ($\tilde{M}$), of the population mean of the class in which the score falls ($\tilde{M}_c$), and of the remaining or residual aspect which is attributable to various uncontrolled sources of variation called random errors (e). In a one-way classification the $\tilde{M}_c$ component is an expression of the difference between a class mean and the over-all mean. Similarly the e for a given score is an expression of the fact that it deviates from the mean of the class in which it falls plus the difference between the class mean and the over-all mean. Random errors may be due to a variety of factors, such as uncontrolled variation of the unit measured, the method of measuring, or the conditions under which the measurement is taken. If the random errors can be considered to be uncorrelated and normally distributed and to have the same variation for each class, the P-value and confidence limits of R can be estimated.

Thus, assuming that the components of any score x (namely, $\tilde{M}$, $\tilde{M}_c$, and e) are additive,

$$x = \tilde{M} + \tilde{M}_c + e$$

However, we are not here interested in the value of $\tilde{M}$ in the population since it does not vary, nor do we wish to test whether it is greater than zero. Rather we are interested in analyzing the deviations of the x's, and hence also the $\tilde{M}_c$'s and e's from the over-all $\tilde{M}$.

Let us for the moment assume that C is a random classification. Let us also assume that the deviations of the $\tilde{M}_c$'s and e's are normally and independently distributed with a mean of zero and variances σ_c^2 and σ_e^2 respectively. These variances are the expected mean squares of the components, in terms of which we may express the variance of the x's thus:

$$\sigma_x^2 = \sigma_c^2 + \sigma_e^2$$

The calculation of the components of variance for a one-way classification can now be illustrated in terms of the expected mean squares, that is, the $E(MS)$. The $E(MS)$ are estimated from the mean squares (i.e., the MS) of the analysis of variance table, and they provide a method for estimating the respective components of variance. Furthermore, the *MS* equal the *E(MS)* in a probability (not algebraic) sense, in so far as they would converge to what the *MS* are expected to be "in the long run" if the experiment were repeated an indefinitely large number of times.

The appropriate *E(MS)* for the first two examples are given as a part of the summary of findings for Tables 1 and 2. In Table 1 the *E(MS)* for within classes is σ_e^2, and for between classes it is $\sigma_e^2 + 5\sigma_c^2$. The component of variance $\hat{\sigma}_e^2$ is given directly in the analysis of variance table and is 9.28 (the $\wedge$ on any σ^2 signifies that it is an unbiased estimate). The component of variance for between classes may be obtained by the following rule: Subtract the mean squares for the residual (*WMS*) from the mean squares for classes (*BCMS*) and divide by the coefficient of the component of variance for classes, which in this example is 5. (The coefficient for classification *C* is the value of *k*.) Thus the component of variance $\hat{\sigma}_c^2$ is estimated as follows: $(170.27 - 9.28)/5$, which is 32.20. From these components of variance we can estimate *R* directly by using formula **3**:

$$R = \frac{\sigma_c^2}{\sigma_c^2 + \sigma_e^2} \doteq \frac{32.20}{32.20 + 9.28} = .78$$

where the symbol $\doteq$ means "is estimated by."

Similarly the components of variance for the data in Table 2 are $\hat{\sigma}_e^2 = 41.17$, and $\hat{\sigma}_c^2 = (364.07 - 41.17)/9.93 = 32.52$. (It will be noted that in computing the component of variance for $\hat{\sigma}_c^2$ in Table 2, $\bar{k}$ is substituted for *k*, which was used in Table 1.) The *R* of .44 may be estimated from the appropriate components of variance as follows:

$$R = \frac{\sigma_c^2}{\sigma_c^2 + \sigma_e^2} \doteq \frac{32.52}{32.52 + 41.17} = .44$$

In the above discussion it was assumed that the *C* classification is a random variate. Actually, in the one-way classification *C* may be either random or fixed, since in either case σ_e^2 is estimated on the basis of the within-class scores and σ_c^2 is estimated on the basis of the between-class means. In other words, it is assumed that the scores within classes are indistinguishable with respect to *k* levels of *K*. If *K* is fixed, as in the example involving friendship *pairs*, **repeated** sampling would increase only the levels of C. Or, if an investigator could assign scores indicating preference for a political candidate, C would be fixed and probably set at 2 (in this country, not France), and repeated sampling would involve increasing the levels of K. In a one-way classification, R could be computed also if both C and K were random. If C and K were both fixed, and all of the possible cases were exhausted, R could be computed as a descriptive measure, but the estimation of P-values and confidence limits would not be in order, since inferences beyond the data being analyzed would have no meaning. The fact that the C or K classifications are fixed or random (from a finite or infinite population) would, however, determine the investigator's interpretation of his findings.

2. the two-way classification[3]

If the assumptions involving the conditions of the data and the experimental design mentioned previously are met, we may generalize the use of the analysis of variance, and hence of R, to the two-way classification. Thus we can assume that all the information that we can learn by proper analysis of the data concerning any particular score (x) is a linear function of: the over-all mean $(\tilde{M})$, the mean of the class in which the score falls $(\tilde{M}_c)$, the mean of the level of k in which the score falls $(\tilde{M}_k)$, the interaction effect of a given level of c with a given level of k $(\tilde{M}_{ck})$, and the remaining or residual aspect which can be attributed to uncontrolled or random errors (e). If the components of x, namely, $\tilde{M}$, $\tilde{M}_c$, $\tilde{M}_k$, $\tilde{M}_{ck}$, and e are additive,

$$x = \tilde{M} + \tilde{M}_c + \tilde{M}_k + \tilde{M}_{ck} + e$$

Again let us assume that the deviations of the c's, k's, ck's, and e's are normally and independently distributed with a mean of zero

---

[3] Extensions of the analysis of variance model to more complex designs, such as the various nonfactorial two-way and three-way models (such as hierarchal models) are beyond the scope of our present discussion. However, the details of a variety of such designs may be found in the following sources: Snedecor (1956); Anderson and Bancroft (1952); Kempthorne (1952); Lindquist (1953); Harter and Lum (1955); Wilk and Kempthorne (1955); and Scheffé (1956). The general factorial three-way model is given in Table 7, Chapter VI.

and variances σ_c^2, σ_k^2, σ_{ck}^2, and σ_e^2. These are the possible variance components for the two-way classification, in terms of which we may express the variances of the x's thus:

$$\sigma_x^2 = \sigma_c^2 + \sigma_k^2 + \sigma_{ck}^2 + \sigma_e^2$$

These components of variance will be estimated and used to form the ratios necessary to estimate the appropriate R's from a variety of explicit experimental designs.

The use of randomization is particularly important in the two-way classification. In the random and mixed models, randomization enters the experimental procedure in that the levels for the C and/or K classifications are selected at random from the larger population. But in any case the procedure of randomization should be used in assigning different experimental units at random to each cell, that is, to each combination of the C and K levels. Randomization is thus used as insurance in connection with the assumption mentioned previously that the random errors should be normally distributed, have a common variance, and be uncorrelated among themselves and with the C and K classifications. In designs in which the same persons appear in two or more cells and/or are measured on two or more variables which are correlated among themselves in the population, it is questionable whether the above assumption is met; consequently the meaning of the analysis of this type of data is open to question if

TABLE 4

Summary of Expected Mean Squares and Proper Error Terms for Two-Way Classification Designs Assuming Randomness of Scores within Cells

Classification	Mean Square	$E(MS)$	Proper Error Term
C	$BCMS$	$\sigma_e^2 + \left(\dfrac{K-k}{K}\right)s\sigma_{ck}^2 + sk\sigma_c^2$	$\left(\dfrac{K-k}{K}\right)I + \dfrac{k}{K}R'$
K	$BKMS$	$\sigma_e^2 + \left(\dfrac{C-c}{C}\right)s\sigma_{ck}^2 + sc\sigma_k^2$	$\left(\dfrac{C-c}{C}\right)I + \dfrac{c}{C}R'$
$CK = I$	IMS	$\sigma_e^2 + s\sigma_{ck}^2$	R'
R'	$R'MS$	σ_e^2	

Note: The components of variance (σ_c^2, σ_k^2, σ_{ck}^2, and σ_e^2) and coefficients (c, k, and s) are as previously defined. The symbol $R'MS$ is used to designate the residual mean square estimated from the within-cell variation when $s \geqslant 2$; when $s = 1$, $R'MS$ would become RMS. s indicates the number of scores per cell.

experimental designs such as we are considering here are used. When this assumption is violated, the general effect will be to change the error term, and hence the significance of the effects to some unknown degree. Possible methods for avoiding violation of the above assumption will be discussed later in this chapter and in Chapters VI and VII.

In estimating R and F from data in the form of a two-way classification it is necessary first to determine the proper mean squares for each classification, the interaction, and the error term appropriate to any particular experimental design. On the assumption that the units within cells are sampled at random from an infinite population, the appropriate estimates for the $E(MS)$ and error terms for the fixed, random, and mixed models are summarized in Table 4.[4]

In estimating F for the fixed model, the proper error term may be determined from Table 4 as follows: for classification C, with K fixed and equal to, say, 3, $[(3 - 3)/3]I + \frac{3}{3}R'$, so that the proper error term for C (and also for K and I) in a fixed model is R' (σ_e^2).

By the same procedure, for the random model the proper error term for classifications C and K is the interaction mean square: IMS ($\sigma_e^2 + s\sigma_{ck}^2$).

Similarly, for the mixed model, assuming that C is random and K is fixed, the proper error term for classification C is $R'MS$ (σ_e^2), and the proper error term for classification K is IMS ($\sigma_e^2 + s\sigma_{ck}^2$). If, however, classification C is fixed and K is random, the proper error term for classification C is IMS ($\sigma_e^2 + s\sigma_{ck}^2$), and the proper error term for classification K is $R'MS$ (σ_e^2).

It is apparent that whenever $R'MS$ is the proper error term the component σ_e^2 must be based on the variation within cells, in which case it is necessary that two or more scores should exist in each cell.

R may be estimated directly from the appropriate components of variance, which can be obtained by the rule: Subtract from the mean square for which the component of variance, σ^2, is desired the mean

---

[4] The method for estimating the $E(MS)$, components of variance, and proper error terms presented here is congruent with the theory and formulations given by Anderson and Bancroft (1952); Harter and Lum (1955); and Wilk and Kempthorne (1955); and Table 4 is adapted from Tables 2 and 3, pp. 1152–1153, of Wilk and Kempthorne (1955).

square which contains the identical remaining terms, and divide the difference by the product of the coefficients associated with the desired σ^2. The component σ_e^2 is given by the $R'MS$; the coefficient for the component σ_{ck}^2 is s, the number of units or scores per cell; and the coefficients of the components σ_k^2 and σ_c^2 are the product of s and the number of levels in the alternate classification. Thus estimates of the individual components of variance for Table 4 are obtained as follows:

$$\sigma_e^2 \doteq R'MS$$

$$\sigma_{ck}^2 \doteq \frac{IMS - R'MS}{s}$$

$$\sigma_k^2 \doteq \frac{BKMS - IMS}{sc}$$

$$\sigma_c^2 \doteq \frac{BCMS - IMS}{sk}$$

(For more detailed discussions of the estimation and interpretation of components of variance see, for example, Daniels, 1939; Crump, 1946; Satterthwaite, 1946; Fisher, 1950; Cochran, 1951; Crump, 1951; Kendall, 1951, 1952; Tukey, 1951; Anderson and Bancroft, 1952; Hald, 1952a; Kempthorne, 1952; Lindquist, 1953; Nelder, 1954; Harter and Lum, 1955; Lowry, 1955; Schultz, 1955; and Snedecor, 1956.)

Since a component of variance is an estimate of variation, it is to be expected that a component cannot take a value which is less than zero. Occasionally, and in most designs presumably as a result of sampling errors, a σ^2 is estimated to have a negative value. For such cases we shall follow the practice of arbitrarily placing the value of such a component at 0. In estimating R's and F's we could, of course, work with components of variance which have a negative sign, and in certain analysis of variance designs this practice has been recommended (cf. Nelder, 1954, and footnote on p. 116).

The estimation of R as a ratio of components of variance can now be illustrated with the findings summarized in Table 3. Assuming that Table 3 represents either a random model or a fixed model with the CK interaction equal to zero (since $s = 1$), we find from the analysis of the data in terms of the two-way classification: $\hat{\sigma}_{ck}^2 = 72.33$; $\hat{\sigma}_c^2 = 247.77$; and $\hat{\sigma}_k^2 = 42.63$. From these values we may estimate the following R's:

$$R_c = \frac{\sigma_c^2}{\sigma_c^2 + \sigma_{ck}^2} \doteq \frac{247.77}{247.77 + 72.33} = .77$$

$$R_k = \frac{\sigma_k^2}{\sigma_k^2 + \sigma_{ck}^2} \doteq \frac{42.63}{42.63 + 72.33} = .37$$

In this example it is not possible to estimate R_{ck}, since the component of variance σ_e^2, based on within-cells variation, is not available.

In Table 3 an R of .68 was computed in terms of the one-way classification. This R has no definite meaning, since the WMS, which is appropriate for the one-way classification, is overestimated if an order effect exists. However, in this example we can determine the extent of the bias in the component of variance based on the variation within classes, $\hat{\sigma}_{wc}^2$, which is just the value of $\hat{\sigma}_k^2$. In other words, $\hat{\sigma}_{ck}^2 + \hat{\sigma}_k^2 = \hat{\sigma}_{wc}^2$ or, arithmetically, $72.33 + 42.63 = 114.96$ (because of rounding errors). We can also look at the extent of the bias in σ_{wc}^2 in terms of the magnitude of the order effect, in which case we find it to be "significant" at the .05 level (F for 4 and 12 $df = 3.36$), as shown in Table 3.

From Table 4 it is apparent that the proper F-test for C, K, or CK in any particular experimental design requires the use of the proper error term. Thus, depending on *whether the investigator has used a fixed, a random, or a mixed model in a two-way classification, there is one and only one appropriate F-test for any given comparison, and the definition of this F can be specified without ambiguity.* When the $E(MS)$ in Table 4 are written out, it will be seen that the $E(MS)$ for the numerator of F contains only one term in addition to the otherwise identical terms in the $E(MS)$ which forms the denominator (i.e., the proper error term) of the F. Furthermore, because of the relation of R to F, there is correspondingly one and only one appropriate R possible for any given comparison in relation to C, K or CK, depending on whether a fixed, random, or mixed model is used. It is also apparent that, in some cases, a particular R or F cannot be

TABLE 5

Appropriate F's and R's for Various Two-Way Classifications under Assumptions Specified in Connection with Table 4†

Classification

	F		R	
	MS	E(MS)	MS	Components
Fixed model $(C = c; K = k)$				
C	$\dfrac{BCMS}{R'MS}$	$\dfrac{\sigma_e^2 + sk\sigma_c^2}{\sigma_e^2}$	$\dfrac{BCMS - R'MS}{BCMS + (k-1)R'MS}$	$\dfrac{\sigma_c^2}{\sigma_c^2 + \sigma_e^2}$
K	$\dfrac{BKMS}{R'MS}$	$\dfrac{\sigma_e^2 - sc\sigma_k^2}{\sigma_e^2}$	$\dfrac{BKMS + R'MS}{BKMS + (k-1)R'MS}$	$\dfrac{\sigma_k^2}{\sigma_k^2 + \sigma_e^2}$
$\begin{array}{l}CK\\ = I\end{array}$	$\dfrac{IMS}{R'MS}$	$\dfrac{\sigma_e^2 + s\sigma_{ck}^2}{\sigma_e^2}$	$\dfrac{IMS - R'MS}{IMS + (k-1)R'MS}$	$\dfrac{\sigma_{ck}^2}{\sigma_{ck}^2 + \sigma_e^2}$
Random model $(C = \infty; K = \infty)$				
C	$\dfrac{BCMS}{IMS}$	$\dfrac{\sigma_e^2 + s\sigma_{ck}^2 + sk\sigma_c^2}{\sigma_e^2 + s\sigma_{ck}^2}$	$\dfrac{BCMS - IMS}{BCMS + (k-1)IMS}$	$\dfrac{\sigma_c^2}{\sigma_c^2 + \sigma_{ck}^2 + \sigma_e^2}$
K	$\dfrac{BKMS}{IMS}$	$\dfrac{\sigma_e^2 + s\sigma_{ck}^2 + sc\sigma_k^2}{\sigma_e^2 + s\sigma_{ck}^2}$	$\dfrac{BKMS - IMS}{BKMS + (k-1)IMS}$	$\dfrac{\sigma_k^2}{\sigma_k^2 + \sigma_{ck}^2 + \sigma_e^2}$
$\begin{array}{l}CK\\ = I\end{array}$	$\dfrac{IMS}{R'MS}$	$\dfrac{\sigma_e^2 + s\sigma_{ck}^2}{\sigma_e^2}$	$\dfrac{IMS - R'MS}{IMS + (k-1)R'MS}$	$\dfrac{\sigma_{ck}^2}{\sigma_{ck}^2 + \sigma_e^2}$

Mixed model
$(C = \infty; K = k)$
C (same as fixed model)
K (same as random model)
$CK = I$ (same as fixed or random model)

Mixed model
$(C = c; K = \infty)$
C (same as random model)
K (same as fixed model)
$CK = I$ (same as fixed or random model)

---

† Some authors designate the component corresponding to a fixed classification differently from one corresponding to a random classification. Thus Anderson and Bancroft (1952) in discussing both fixed and mixed models use the symbol θ to indicate a fixed effect and σ^2 to indicate a random effect. But, since R may be estimated whether a classification is fixed or random, the symbol σ^2 is used throughout this table for convenience and consistency.

estimated unless more than one score exists in each cell or unless the "interaction effect" can be assumed to be zero and the IMS used in place of $R'MS$. In case of doubt, however, the IMS may be used, with the awareness that the resulting R or F may be underestimated. Finally, unless $R'MS$ is available, an F or R based on the IMS cannot be estimated at all.

In estimating R in terms of the components of variance, which may be obtained from the $E(MS)$ in Table 4, the last component on the right is placed in the numerator and all the components in that $E(MS)$ are placed in the denominator. Or R may be estimated directly from the appropriate F or from the appropriate mean squares.

In summary, given the conditions that the levels of the C and/or K classifications either represent all the possible levels from a small finite population of levels (i.e., they are fixed variates) or are randomly sampled from a very large, or infinite, population of levels (i.e., they are random variates), and that the experimental units (s) in each cell are greater than one and are drawn at random from a large population of such units, we may then define the possible appropriate F's and R's that may be estimated from the various two-way classifications. This is done in Table 5, which makes explicit the principles summarized in Table 4.

Because of the large number of F's and R's that may be estimated from the various two-way classifications, no attempt will be made to give substantive illustrations which correspond to each of the cases specified in Table 5. However, a few remarks concerning the fixed, random, and mixed models may serve to indicate the types of situations in which R may be computed as a meaningful statistic. When the fixed model is used, R probably will not be estimated in most cases, because, by definition, the investigator is primarily interested in studying the effects of particular fixed conditions, as in controlled experimentation. In some cases, however, R may be computed as a measure of the consistency or homogeneity of scores or, when the number of scores in each cell is large, as an index of the strength of certain nomothetic relations among the fixed conditions used in the experiment. In the random model all the components in the $E(MS)$ are random variance components, in terms of which R may be defined. Consequently this model is ideally suited to the study of certain problems, such as the estimation of test reliability. Various considerations involved in estimating reliability will be discussed in Chapter VI. In general, however, the mixed model is probably applicable to the widest range of research problems, and we shall consider one of these, pattern analysis, in Chapter VII.

But, even though the analysis of variance models summarized in Table 5 are sufficiently comprehensive to cover a large number of research designs, it is necessary first to examine certain important special cases involving two-way classifications before considering the estimation of reliability and the analysis of test profiles.

D. SOME SPECIAL CASES INVOLVING TWO-WAY CLASSIFICATIONS

1. where the "finite population correction factor" (fpc) should be used

In the previous discussion we considered the role of this correction factor in the two limiting cases: when a classification is fixed, and when it is random. We saw that if a classification is fixed the interaction component for the alternate classification is reduced to 0, whereas if the classification is random the alternate interaction term remains unaffected. It frequently occurs, however, that the levels of one or both of the classifications are selected at random from a small finite number of possible levels. Under such conditions the investigator should use the finite population correction factor to estimate the $E(MS)$ and the proper error term before computing R or F. It is also worth noting that the use of this correction reduces the size of the component for the interaction term, and thus avoids underestimation of the main effects.

Table 6 is presented as an illustration of the use of the finite population correction factor with data which represent the relative amount of space given to 25 subject matter categories ($c = 25$) in five

TABLE 6

The Transformed Scores for Space Given to Twenty-Five Topics by Each of Five Textbooks in Educational Psychology

Topic	Author 1	2	3	4	5	Sum (x)
1	6.80	6.02	0.00	5.65	11.39	29.86
2	7.49	0.00	7.27	12.66	9.10	36.52
3	11.97	4.52	16.32	4.29	15.45	52.55
4	11.97	0.00	9.28	14.18	12.39	47.82
5	8.33	0.00	7.49	14.77	7.92	38.51
6	18.15	21.13	15.00	7.71	15.45	77.44
7	10.14	6.80	9.98	10.63	8.13	45.68
8	16.64	7.27	12.25	16.22	12.79	65.17
9	10.31	12.39	12.79	12.11	10.47	58.07
10	14.65	25.10	7.92	21.47	15.68	84.82
11	20.79	23.50	32.14	24.50	14.54	115.47
12	11.39	5.53	3.63	6.02	10.47	37.04
13	12.66	10.63	8.33	10.14	9.10	50.86
14	13.56	9.10	18.44	13.31	11.54	65.95
15	12.39	9.10	7.27	13.56	10.78	53.10
16	2.07	0.00	0.00	0.00	11.09	13.16
17	3.53	0.00	0.00	0.00	6.80	10.33
18	1.72	0.00	4.66	5.53	20.00	31.91
19	6.02	15.56	7.27	13.44	7.71	50.00
20	4.73	9.63	13.69	8.91	7.04	44.00
21	6.02	2.75	9.28	4.29	12.11	34.45
22	11.24	18.63	4.17	10.63	10.14	54.81
23	10.94	12.39	8.13	7.04	5.50	44.00
24	16.74	16.54	17.05	11.54	14.65	76.52
25	13.05	6.29	6.02	0.00	5.13	30.49
Sum (x)	263.30	222.88	238.38	248.60	275.37	1,248.53
Sum (x^2)	3359.07	3403.35	3429.35	3378.05	3343.47	16,913.29

Summary of Findings

Source of Variation	SS	df	MS	Random Model $(C = \infty; K = \infty)$ E(MS)	R	Mixed Model $(c = C; k = 1/3K)$ E(MS)	R
Total	4442.67	124					
Topics $(c = 25)$	2481.58	24	103.40	$0 + \sigma_{ck}^2 + 5\sigma_c^2$	.46	$0 + \left(\dfrac{15-5}{15}\right)\sigma_{ck}^2 + 5\sigma_c^2$	.58
Authors $(k = 5)$	67.70	4	16.93	(of no interest)		(of no interest)	
Interaction (ck)	1893.39	96	19.72	$0 + \sigma_{ck}^2$		$0 + \left(\dfrac{15-5}{15}\right)\sigma_{ck}^2$	
Residual				$(\sigma_e^2 = 0)$		$(\sigma_e^2 = 0)$	

educational psychology textbooks ($k = 5$) published in 1948.[5] We may then ask, "What is the correlation among these texts (or to what extent do they agree) in the amount of space given to the subject matter categories?" But, before starting to answer this question, certain characteristics of the data should be noted, such as the fact that originally they were tabulated as the percentage of space given to each topic. Also in the reported percentage data the k sums range from 96.09 to 125.82, indicating that some passages were tabulated under more than one category and, furthermore, the k means and the variances are highly correlated ($r = .98$). Since the variation among the k means is irrelevant to our question, and the k means and variances should be uncorrelated, the arc sine transformation (see Snedecor, 1956, pp. 318–319) is applied to the original percentage data. The scores thus transformed are presented in Table 6.

Let us assume that both the C and K classifications are random, so that the analysis of variance model for Table 6 is random. It is convenient for our purposes here to make this assumption in order to use the "interaction" as the proper error term. From the summary of findings, it is apparent that in the random model $\hat{\sigma}_{ck}^2 = 19.72$ and $\hat{\sigma}_c^2 = (103.40 - 19.72)/5 = 16.74$. Consequently in this case

$$R = \frac{\sigma_c^2}{\sigma_c^2 + \sigma_{ck}^2} \doteq \frac{16.74}{16.74 + 19.72} = \frac{16.74}{36.46} = .46$$

and

$$F = \frac{\sigma_{ck}^2 + 5\sigma_c^2}{\sigma_{ck}^2} \doteq \frac{19.72 + 5(16.74)}{19.72} = \frac{103.40}{19.72} = 5.24$$

---

[5] The five books are by Woodruff, Davis, Peterson *et al.*, Gates *et al.*, and Crow and Crow. Although 26 categories were listed in the tables cited, no ratings were given for adult education; hence the number of categories was reduced to 25. Furthermore, it was observed that 0 per cent of space was recorded for some text categories, indicating that those texts did not discuss those categories. In computing R, however, $k = 5$ for all 25 classes, since, when a text does not deal with a topic, the obtained score is 0 per cent. If data had not been available on some texts in relation to some topics, $\bar{k}$ would have been required. I am grateful to Dr. Glenn M. Blair (1949) for permission to adapt the published data for Table 6.

In this example we have no interest in any differences due to authors, which are artifacts of the method of transforming the raw percentage data—except that we have equalized by the analysis of variance technique any differences in the k means due to the transformation.

If, however, there were a finite number of textbooks in educational psychology, and we found that it would be too time consuming (or tedious) to categorize the subject matter content of all of them, we could select at random a sample of the total number and still estimate the correlation. Let us suppose that we are interested only in the 25 topics that were used, so that the C classification is fixed, and also that there are only 15 such texts in all, and that five of the 15 had been selected at random, so that the K classification is random. If the data in Table 6 had been obtained under these conditions, we would need to apply the finite population correction (fpc) to the interaction component, which correction is given in the summary of findings in Table 6 for the mixed model. From this summary (or from Table 4) it is seen that $\hat{\sigma}_{ck}^2 = ([15 - 5]/15)(19.72) = 13.15$, and $\hat{\sigma}_c^2 = (103.40 - 13.15)/5 = 18.05$. Consequently, when the fpc of $\frac{2}{3}$ is applied,

$$R = \frac{\sigma_c^2}{\sigma_c^2 + \sigma_{ck}^2} \doteq \frac{18.05}{18.05 + 13.15} = \frac{18.05}{31.20} = .58$$

and

$$F = \frac{\sigma_{ck}^2 + 5\sigma_c^2}{\sigma_{ck}^2} \doteq \frac{13.15 + 5(18.05)}{13.15} = \frac{103.40}{13.15} = 7.86$$

and again we have no interest in any variation among the authors. When the R's and F's are compared, it is apparent that, if a larger number of the books had been rated, say ten, the estimated values of R and F would have been raised still further (specifically, R would be .75 and F would be 15.74). If all the books had been rated, σ_{ck}^2 would be 0, so that R would be $+1$ and F would be ∞.

In certain respects Table 6 is not a good example of the use of fpc, simply because $s = 1$, so that an estimate of σ_e^2 is not available from the data. Rather we have assumed that the error term is 0. As a consequence, the above-mentioned R of $+1$ cannot be interpreted in the usual sense, but rather as due to the absence of uncontrolled sources of variation, which follows from the assumption that $\sigma_e^2 = 0$ in this case. In terms of formula 3, R would be defined as the ratio

$$\frac{\sigma_c^2}{\sigma_c^2 + 0} = 1$$

In connection with Tables 4 and 5, when all 15 texts are rated on all 25 categories, the analysis of variance model is fixed; this in turn requires an estimate of σ_e^2. The above difficulty would be removed, of course, if s were 2 or more in each cell in Table 6, in which case R would take a meaningful value. (The question of $\sigma_e^2 = 0$ will be considered again in the next section.)

Returning to the value of $R = .46$, it is of interest to compare this value with the average of the ten r's obtained by correlating each pair of texts separately. These r's range from .20 to .69, and their average (through the z transformation) is .47 after suitable corrections have been applied (cf. Fisher, 1950). In terms of Property 7 of R, Chapter III, we would expect that $R = \bar{r}$; the reason for the slight discrepancy is that the k variances differ slightly in the transformed percentage data in Table 6. If, however, the variances had been equalized arithmetically, we would expect any differences between R and $\bar{r}$ to be due to errors of rounding only.

Any evaluation of the R of .46 (which is significant at less than the .01 level) must be made in the context of the particular research problem, data, and interests of the investigator. In the example just given it should be remembered that this R is a description of the over-all degree of agreement among the 5 texts written by different authors, and that authors are not expected to concur as to how space should be apportioned to the various topics. If, however, this R were based on the ratings of a single text by 5 judges, it might indicate the need for more precise definitions of the categories and/or an increase in the scoring ability of one or more of the judges. In such a case, even though the degree of consistency is statistically significant, an R of .46 may or may not be sufficiently high to meet the requirements of the investigator.

We have seen that the finite population correction factor should be used in cases where the possible number of levels in the C and/or

K classification is relatively small—but where it is also impossible, impractical, or too expensive or time consuming to study all the possible levels. Furthermore, when the possible number of units (s) per cell is a small finite number, it is likewise proper to apply the correction $(S - s)/S$ in estimating the error term σ_e^2. This practice is customarily followed in sample survey research (cf. Cochran, 1953; Hansen et al., 1953); in fact, it was in this context that the *fpc* was first used.

An example of the application of the *fpc* in the case of the more typical observational or experimental setting might involve, for example, a study of the relative effectiveness of four teachers in modifying attitudes toward minority groups in a "human relations" course, as inferred from projective test protocols. If there are, say, 30 pupils in each of the four classrooms, this is the "finite population" we are concerned with—not the "population" of teachers and/or pupils at large. In this example it would be expensive and time consuming to administer and score the tests for all the pupils in each of the four classrooms. However, if ten pupils were drawn at random from each classroom, the error term in Table 4 would become $\frac{2}{3}$ σ_e^2, or if 20 pupils were studied it would become $\frac{1}{3}$ σ_e^2. If, however, all 30 pupils in each classroom were studied, the error term would vanish, so that any observed differences would be "statistically significant". Or, more properly, statistical inference would be meaningless in such a case, since we would already have all the relevant information.

2. where the $R'MS$ cannot be estimated from the data

In discussing Table 6 it was necessary at one point to assume a random model in order that the interaction term could be used to estimate R and F. This was done to illustrate the fact that an independent estimate of σ_e^2 is a necessity in certain specific cases. It was also suggested that the assumption that $\sigma_e^2 = 0$ is unjustified, as evidenced in the fact that, in the percentage data, the k sums ranged from 96.5 to 125.8 per cent. Since certain sections of the text must have been scored under more than one category to obtain a sum greater than 100 per cent, judgment as to allocation was involved—which presumably might vary for one rater over time or among different raters.

An estimate of the $R'MS$, or σ_e^2, might be obtained in such cases by having the same judge rescore all the texts after a sufficiently long period so that memory of previous scoring could be ruled out, or by obtaining a partial or complete replication of the data by having a number of judges score various book-topic classifications selected at random. However, if a second judge scored all the books on all the categories, one should use a three-way classification since possible differences between judges is a source of variation which can be isolated and which may be of interest in its own right. In this case the estimate of σ_e^2 would be the three-way interaction term (see Table 7, Chapter VI).

In various other situations, however, it may not be possible to obtain an estimate of σ_e^2 from the data because of various practical considerations. An important class of such situations occurs when one desires to estimate the similarity of profiles of scores from a test which yields a set of subscores. If, for example, a clinic patient is given a Wechsler-Bellevue intelligence test, it is usually for the purpose of enabling the clinician to make practical judgments regarding possible treatment. If the clinician also wishes to compare the ten subtest scores of two or more patients, it is not possible to estimate σ_e^2 from the data, since we would again have only one score per cell in a $c = 10$ by $k \geqslant 2$ matrix. Furthermore, the clinician usually is not able to have the patients return at a later date to retake the test. This situation is characteristic of many pattern analytic studies.

It is important to note, however, that, if the published "norms" on such tests as the Wechsler-Bellevue or Minnesota Multiphasic Personality Inventory are based on "populations" which do not differ appreciably from the "sample" of subjects being studied, such norms may be used to provide the estimate of σ_e^2, because σ_e^2 is, in fact, the square of the "standard error of measurement," which can be obtained from the test-retest reliability coefficient and the standard deviation of the distribution of scores on each of the subtests (cf. McNemar, 1955, pp. 290–294). This method of estimating σ_e^2 has an additional advantage, namely, that the number of df upon which its estimation is based is much larger than would be available even if it could be estimated from the $c \times k$ matrix. Thus in this case it is not only necessary but also desirable to estimate σ_e^2 from the "standard error of measurement" based on a large number of df by utilizing published norms. This method will be illustrated in Chapter VII.

3. where $BCMS = 0$ when $K = \infty$

By virtue of the manner in which most of the tests which yield a set of scores are standardized, the mean, and the standard deviation, of each of the subtests have a common value. The Wechsler-Bellevue test, for example, is so standardized that each of the ten subtests has a mean of 10 and a standard deviation of 3 for a large representative group of subjects (i.e., the "population"). This suggests that, if we were to sample at random k individuals and administer the set of c subtests to each individual, the between-classes mean square $(BCMS)$ computed in terms of the subtests would approach 0 as k increased. Or, in other words, we must assume that $BCMS = 0$ in the population. This fact requires some reconsideration of how R might be estimated and interpreted whenever tests of this type are to be used in pattern analytic studies.

One solution is to consider a mixed analysis of variance model where C (the subtests) is fixed and K (the individuals) is random, and to estimate R_{ck} instead of R_c as a meaningful measure of similarity or dissimilarity in the set of profiles being studied. That is to say, since the expectation is that the component σ_c^2 will be 0, the component σ_{ck}^2 will be small when the profiles are similar and will be large when the profiles are dissimilar. Specifically, assuming for the present no differences among the k means (usually called differences in profile "level"), the component σ_{ck}^2 will be minimal when the scores for each subtest (i.e., level of C) are identical, and σ_{ck}^2 will be maximal when the scores for each subtest differ maximally. In the former case, we would say that the k sets of scores have the "same pattern." We have seen from Tables 4 and 5 that an estimate of σ_e^2 is required to estimate an R or F based on σ_{ck}^2.

If the σ_{ck}^2 is used to indicate similarities or differences in score profiles, it is convenient to make the assumption that the minimal value that any component of variance may take is 0. Thus, when $\sigma_{ck}^2 = 0$, R may be estimated by formula **3** as $0/(0 + \sigma_e^2)$, which equals 0. Correspondingly, as σ_{ck}^2 approaches its maximal value in relation to σ_e^2, R will approach $+1$. This finding differs from our usual conception of the use of a measure of correlation as an index of agreement or disagreement, since we usually consider that a value near $+1$ indicates a high degree of agreement and that a value near 0 indicates lack of agreement.

This inversion can be rectified by defining R_P, a measure of similarity of score profiles, as $1 - R_{ck}$.[6] If this is done, $R_P = +1.00$ when the within subtest scores are identical in a one-way classification, or are equalized by the analysis of variance technique in a two-way classification. However, in estimating the P-value and confidence limits of R_P, we must use the $F = IMS/R'MS$ with the appropriate *df*. If this F is statistically significant at a specified level of confidence, it will indicate a *departure from agreement* among the k profiles, and in that sense will correspond directly to R_{ck} and inversely to $R_P = 1 - R_{ck}$. Various uses of R in pattern analytic studies will be discussed in more detail in Chapter VII.

4. where an obtained R may be negative

In the large majority of cases the obtained value of R will be positive. If R is computed from formula **3** (which is the basic definition of R, based on the one-way classification with the value of K unlimited), R cannot take a value less than 0, since the ratio $\sigma_c^2/(\sigma_c^2 + \sigma_e^2)$ must be 0 or positive.[7] Thus the components of vari-

---

[6] It is interesting to note that, if this formulation were applied to the problem of estimating the reliability of measures, it would result in a statement such as: "The degree of reliability is satisfactory if the two or more sets of measures do not differ significantly."

[7] In connection with the classical example of the use of R, namely, the correlation of heights of brothers within a family, some restriction is required on the upper limit of K. Although it is clear that the possible number of brothers in a family is not unlimited, the theoretical upper limit is not known.

ance, which are estimates of variation, cannot be negative. If estimates of σ^2 are computed to have a negative value, they are arbitrarily set at 0, on the assumption that the negative value must be due to sampling errors. However, in discussing Property 4 of R, it was observed that R may take a meaningful negative value in certain cases, particularly when the possible number of levels of K in the "population" is a small finite number, but in any case $\tilde{R}$ cannot be less than $-1/(K-1)$. The example of "friendship pairs" was given to illustrate the case of $K = 2$ in the population, in which case increased sampling from this population will increase the number of such pairs, or levels of C, but will not increase the levels of K.

The occurrence of a meaningful negative R is possible as a result of the extension of the analysis of variance model underlying R from the one-way to the two-way classification. Specifically, we shall consider the case in which a negative R may occur when the data are arranged in a $c \times k$ analysis of variance design with one score per cell (i.e., $s = 1$) entered at random in the design. From Table 4 we may determine the expected mean squares for this $c \times k$ analysis of variance design with $s = 1$ as follows:

Source of Variation	MS	$E(MS)$
C	$BCMS$	$\left(\dfrac{K-k}{K}\right)\sigma_{ck}^2 + k\sigma_c^2$
K	$BKMS$	$\left(\dfrac{C-c}{C}\right)\sigma_{ck}^2 + c\sigma_k^2$
$CK\ (\,=\text{residual})$	IMS	σ_{ck}^2

If C and K are both random, the $E(MS)$ for $BCMS = \sigma_{ck}^2 + k\sigma_c^2$, so that

$$R = \frac{BCMS - IMS}{BCMS + (k-1)\,IMS} = \frac{\sigma_c^2}{\sigma_c^2 + \sigma_{ck}^2}$$

which can be negative only as a result of sampling errors. If, under such conditions, the obtained R is negative, it must be assumed to be not greater than 0.

If, however, K is fixed, $(K - k)/K = 0$, and the $E(MS)$ for $BCMS$ reduces to $k\sigma_c{}^2$. In this case,

$$R = \frac{k\sigma_c{}^2 - \sigma_{ck}{}^2}{k\sigma_c{}^2 + (k - 1)\ \sigma_{ck}{}^2}$$

which is negative when the class means are identical, so that $\sigma_{ck}{}^2 > k\sigma_c{}^2$. It is possible for $\sigma_{ck}{}^2$ to exceed $k\sigma_c{}^2$, especially when the difference between class means $(BCMS)$ is small.[8] Note also that when $k\sigma_c{}^2 = 0$, the above formula reduces to:

$$\frac{0 - \sigma_{ck}{}^2}{0 + (k - 1)\ \sigma_{ck}{}^2} = \frac{-1}{k - 1}$$

which is the minimal value that R may take (see Chapter III, Properties 1 and 2 of R).

Finally, if the scores in each level of C are distributed randomly in terms of the K levels, $c\sigma_k{}^2$ will not be expected to differ from 0, and as the levels of C approach ∞, the $E(MS)$ for $BKMS$ will approach 0. That is to say, there will be no differences among the k means—or, in other words, the within-class scores will be "indistinguishable." Under these conditions the two-way classification will reduce logically and numerically to the one-way classification. Hence the preceding interpretation of negative values of R applies also to the usual one-way analysis.

---

[8] See Chapter V, Special Case 3, where $BCMS = 0$ when $K = \infty$. If an estimate of $\sigma_e{}^2$ is available, it is also possible to obtain an R from a fixed analysis of variance model when $s = 1$. In this case the investigator would be interested in studying only the responses of K individuals (or K responses of one individual) on C subtests. But from Tables 4 and 5 it is apparent that the estimated value of R may differ, depending on whether a fixed, random, or particular mixed model is appropriate. The choice of model depends, of course, on its appropriateness in terms of the design and the investigator's research questions.

VI

the application of intraclass correlation to reliability studies

A. INTRODUCTION

The question of the proper application of any statistic requires some consideration of the range of situations in which its use would be an appropriate technique for summarizing sets of empirical data. The distinction is frequently made in this connection between situations in which the "experimental" versus the "observational" methods are used. Experimentation can be characterized by the fact that the investigator imposes forces, as by experimental controls or treatments, and observes and quantifies their effects. Since the investigator in this case is probably interested in studying the effects of particular experimental treatments, he is apt to use the fixed model design, for which F is generally more appropriate than R. On the other hand, when the observational method is used, the data arise from situations in which the investigator observes phenomena or forces in action and, after making hypotheses as to their nature, quantifies the observed effects of such hypothesized forces. Because of the nature of this methodology, the mixed or random models are more likely to be used, and the questions asked of observational data frequently pertain to the consistency or reliability of observations or measurements, or to the relative similarity of profiles of measures.[1] For research questions such as these, R provides a general measure which may be used to summarize the findings.

The problem of the reliability of measurements is inherent in all science, because whenever man (being fallible) attempts to measure anything there is always the possibility of errors of measurement. In measurement theory it is assumed, of course, that there is a hypothetical "true" measure of the phenomenon in question, and that an obtained measure will be in error to the extent that it deviates from the "true" measure. The sources of error in measurements vary from one method of measurement to another. In considering various possible methods of measurement, it will be helpful to distinguish between (*i*) the object, event, or phenomenon being measured, (*ii*) the device(s) used to obtain the desired measures (e.g., gadgets or tests and persons), and (*iii*) whether each such device remains relatively stable or varies from measurement to measurement.

In the natural sciences it is often assumed that the "object" to be measured always remains stable in relation to the method or "device" used to obtain measurements, so that any errors in measurement can be attributed to the unreliability of the method. A classical example of unreliability in this sense is found in the difference between astronomers in their observation of stellar events, which gave rise to an investigation of the "personal equation" a hundred or

---

[1] The value of the distinction between observational and experimental research is primarily heuristic, since most research involves both methodologies to some degree. Furthermore, there are no clear differences between the two approaches in terms of the possible sophistication of the theory structuring the research, the possible complexity of the phenomena investigated or research design used, the possible precision of the observations or measurements made, or the relevance of such data for answering the questions which instigated the research. If any meaningful distinction exists between these two methods, it is probably one of convenience: in experimentation the investigator is able to control the forces which elicit the phenomena being studied—when he wants them to occur and under what conditions—whereas in observational research the investigator studies phenomena which are more or less beyond his control in this sense.

so years ago. In the measurement of behavior, however, it is impossible to assume that the attributes or behaviors of persons remain, like the stars, so constant that any variation in measurements can be attributed entirely to the unreliability of the measuring device(s).

In the measurement of psychological and other behavioral events, both the phenomena being measured and the measurement device(s) become important sources of variation which contribute to the final measure, and hence to the possible unreliability of it. Consequently it may be misleading or meaningless to speak of *the* "reliability of the test." The complexity of the problem of making psychological measurements is also complicated by the fact that the measuring device itself may vary over time. Thus, if a clinician rates Thematic Apperception Test protocols, he must be thought of as part of the measuring device or method. Only if we could be certain that a clinician or other judge would give the same ratings on the same variables while scoring the same protocols on different occasions could we rule out the judge as an additional source of variation; this, of course, must be considered in estimating the reliability of the measures in such cases. Similarly, in making psychological measurements the investigator may use more than one judge to rate the same set of behaviors, in which case it is apparent that different judges may not appraise identically the behaviors in question, so that, if this source or other sources of variation are present, they also must be considered in the estimation of reliability (cf. Ferguson, 1941; Thorndike *et al.*, 1951, p. 568; Haggard, 1953). It follows that an appropriate method of estimating reliability must be able to account for the various sources of variation or error which are involved in a particular method of measurement.

As a concept, reliability has been defined in various ways and used for a variety of purposes. In 1901 Wissler used the test-retest method of estimating what has come to be called test reliability, although he called it "the precision of a test." The term "reliability coefficient" apparently was coined by Spearman at some time prior to 1910, and at that time he defined it to mean "the coefficient between one half and the other half of several measurements of the same thing" (p. 281).[2] On the basis of a common-sense logic, one might assume from this definition that R, being a univariate statistic, should be used as the appropriate measure of reliability, since "same thing" implies that the data are of the same kind. However, the usual procedure for estimating test reliability, especially in psychological and educational research, has been to compute the bivariate statistic, the product-moment r, and to use this coefficient or some variant of it to describe the reliability of the test.

The appropriateness of r as an estimate of reliability can be questioned on several grounds. It is apparent that r is not sufficiently general to enable the investigator to deal with a variety of possible sources of error. We may also inquire whether it is even appropriate in terms of the methods used to obtain reliability data and the statistical assumptions underlying them. In the following section we shall consider briefly the assumptions underlying the split-half, the parallel- or equivalent-forms, and the test-retest methods for computing r, and, in view of the relevant assumptions, what the proper estimate of the reliability coefficient should be for each method.

B. THE USE OF r AS AN ESTIMATE OF RELIABILITY

The *split-half method* of estimating reliability usually involves giving the whole test at one sitting, then forming equal halves by separating the odd and even items, and then computing r between the scores on the two equal halves of the test. If the two halves are equal, however, it follows that they must have equal means and equal sigmas. Consequently, as Jackson and Ferguson (1941) have shown, the split-half method assumes that the two samples are drawn from a population specified by three parameters: a common mean, a common sigma, and the correlation. It can be shown that the maximum likelihood estimate of the correlation for the three-parameter

---

[2] Wissler (1901, p. 60) observed that "the precision of a test may be estimated by correlating the successive trials." Later Spearman began thinking along similar lines, and in 1910 he and Brown published adjacent papers in the same journal; both used the term "reliability coefficient," but Brown, in his paper, attributed this term to Spearman.

case is identical to R computed by formula **1** (see Appendix IIE for proof). The slight bias in formula **1** is removed by formula **2**, which gives an unbiased estimate of the population correlation, or, in this case, the reliability coefficient based on the split-half method.

The *parallel-forms* and *test-retest methods* require either that two equivalent forms of a test be given separately, or the same test be given twice, with a time interval between the two administrations. The scores of the two tests are then used to compute the reliability coefficient. But, because of the time interval, it is possible that intervening factors such as practice effect and memory may influence equally all the scores in the second trial. Consequently we may assume that, although the two sample sigmas should remain the same, their means may differ. Thus these two methods assume a four-parameter case, namely, a common sigma, the two means, and the correlation. (If both the means and the sigmas differ, the two samples obviously are not measures of the "same thing," at least in a statistical sense; hence some question other than reliability is involved.) The maximum likelihood estimate of the reliability coefficient derived from the four-parameter case (cf. Jackson and Ferguson, 1941) is identical with formula **8**, which estimates R (see Appendix IIF for proof). Thus we see that the coefficient of intraclass correlation should be used as the estimate of test reliability also when the parallel-forms and test-retest methods are used.[3]

But what if an investigator still chooses to compute r as an estimate of test reliability? If he does, at least he should be aware of its several limitations and disadvantages for this purpose. For one thing, we have noted that r is a biased estimator of the population value. But more important is the fact of its inadequacy and inefficiency when more than one source of random errors are involved; this frequently occurs in connection with the measurement of ability and performance. Another general disadvantage of r is that its value is often misleading in terms of the questions that the investigator asks

---

[3] The appropriate maximum likelihood estimates of the reliability coefficients in the population for the three- and the four-parameter cases (when $k = 2$) are also reported in Johnson (1949, p. 125) as formulas 6.36 and 6.35 respectively.

of his data, in as much as any information concerning the means and variances of the two distributions is thrown away in the computation of r. For example, if a test-retest r were computed on data where the scores on the retest were significantly higher and more variable than on the first test, the value of r could still be 1.00, as long as the paired scores held their same relative position in the two distributions. Finally, although the bivariate statistic r may be used in nonreliability cases (i.e., the five-parameter case in which an interclass comparison is made), r is not an appropriate estimator of reliability.

Because coefficients of test reliability usually have been estimated by r, reliability studies have characteristically been based on only two samples of data from each group of subjects. But practical circumstances often make it difficult to obtain large numbers of subjects, with the result that the estimate of the reliability coefficient is much less stable than one would like it to be. Situations of this sort frequently arise, as in state hospitals, where only a small number of patients of a particular clinical type is available for study, but where they are residents for relatively long periods of time.

A solution to this problem may be found by taking several repeated samples from the same subjects and computing the appropriate R. If r were used to obtain measures of reliability (regardless of the question of its appropriateness), it would be necessary to compute $\bar{r}$, the average of the $k(k - 1)/2$ possible r's, in order to take advantage of this situation. However, the R for classes of any size could be obtained directly by formula **2** or **8**, as the situation requires. Furthermore, if some of the subjects in the research sample entered the study after it was under way, or left before it was completed, R could still be obtained directly by computing the appropriate $\bar{k}$ on the basis of all the data collected and using this value in computing R by formula **5**.

Some of the difficulties involved in computing $\bar{r}$ in such cases may be illustrated by the data presented in Table 2. In five of the clubs in this example $k \geqslant 10$, but in the sixth club $k = 3$. One solution might be to discard 43 of the 61 cases (or 70 per cent of the data) and compute $\bar{r}$ on the basis of the three possible r's. But to do this one would have to decide which three scores from each of the first five clubs should be used. One possibility is to select "at random" any three of the available scores in each club. The desirability of selecting scores "at random" (a method which is properly used when one is forced to operate in ignorance) might be open to question in this case, because of the obviously great variation among the scores within classes. This difficulty does not arise in connection with R if $\bar{k}$ is used.

C. THE USE OF R AS AN ESTIMATE OF RELIABILITY

In the theory of mental testing it is assumed that any obtained score (x) is made up of two parts: the "true" score ($\tilde{T}$) plus any "errors of measurement" (e) which cause the obtained scores to differ from the "true" score—or on repeated trials to vary around the "true" score. Reliability then is defined as the ratio

$$\frac{\sigma_{\tilde{T}}^2}{\sigma_x^2} \quad \text{or} \quad \frac{\sigma_{\tilde{T}}^2}{\sigma_{\tilde{T}}^2 + \sigma_e^2} \qquad \text{(See formula 3.)}$$

In these terms a score would be perfectly reliable when $\sigma_e^2 = 0$, so that the ratio would be expressed as a coefficient of $+1$. One of the difficulties involved in estimating the reliability coefficient by r lies in the fact that, if two or more e's are involved in the measurement, r cannot differentiate among them. Consequently, when two or more sources of variation, or error, are present in the measurement situation, the use of r as an estimate of reliability either answers incorrectly, or fails to answer, the investigator's research questions.

In most situations where psychological or other behavioral phenomena are measured, and where estimates of reliability are desired, two or more sources of variation or error are present. It is thus necessary to be able to determine the relative magnitude of each of them if discrete and meaningful estimates of reliability are to be obtained. In view of the discussion in Chapter V, it is apparent that several sources of variation can be expressed as components of variance, and that their relative magnitude can be estimated by the analysis of variance technique to compute the appropriate R's as reliability coefficients.

Important sources of variation in observational research typically have to do with differences among the judges and/or the subjects used in the study. Judge reliability can be thought of in terms of either intrajudge consistency or interjudge concordance, and subject reliability can be thought of in terms of intrasubject stability or intersubject agreement. It is not necessary, however, to consider separately each of the possible types of reliability or various combinations of them. On the contrary, the topics of judge and subject reliability can be subsumed under the general discussion of analysis of variance models, because the fundamental and general questions asked of the data in estimating reliability ultimately pertain to *the relative degree of consistency among sets of intraclass scores*. These questions have been discussed in detail in Chapter V. The estimation of reliability, then, is only a special case of the use of R.

When two or more possible sources of variation are present and can be isolated, R can be used effectively to provide several different estimates of reliability, each of which is appropriate to answer a particular question about the data. Hence various reliability coefficients based on data from studies involving repeated or replicated measures can be readily estimated by R. The measures may be, for example, (*i*) the scores given by several judges to the same material, (*ii*) scores given by one judge to repeated samples from the same subject, (*iii*) scores given by one judge at different times to the same or equivalent materials from the same subject, or (*iv*) scores given by one judge to several representative and presumably equivalent samples from different subjects. In case (*i*) the judges have been replicated and our interest is in interjudge concordance, other things being equal or constant; in case (*ii*) our interest is in the stability of the subject who provides a number of samples of data; in case (*iii*) the consistency of the single judge over intervals of time is involved; and finally in case (*iv*) the agreement among the various subjects is our chief concern. It may be noted that in each of these situations only one of the four sources of variation—judges, tests, trials, subjects—is being considered. In all these situations R gives the most appropriate estimate of reliability by providing suitable controls by the analysis of variance technique to keep any three of the four sources of variation constant if two or more of them are present.

If only one source of variation is present, the data should be analyzed in terms of the one-way classification as described in Chapter V. For example, case ⹁(i) may be illustrated by the data in Table 6 if we assume that five judges rated the protocols of 25 persons on one variable. In this case the only meaningful source of error would be based on the variation among the ratings of the five judges, as estimated by the within-class scores. (If, however, a single judge rated the same materials on five occasions, the example would illustrate case (iii), but there would be no difference in the method of analysis of the data.) We may thus reanalyze the data in Table 6 by considering it to be a 1×25 analysis of variance table with $s = 5$ in each cell.

Source of Variation	SS	df	MS	E(MS)†	R	F	P	90 per cent Confidence Limits
Total	4442.67	124						
Topics	2481.57	24	103.40	$\sigma_{wc}^2 + 5\sigma_c^2$	.46	5.27	.01	.30 – .61
Within classes	1961.10	100	19.61	σ_{wc}^2				

† $\hat{\sigma}_{wc}^2 = 19.61$; $\hat{\sigma}_c^2 = 16.76$.

We can now estimate the R of .46 by formula **2**, **3**, or **6**. It should be noted that the R estimated above and in Table 6 both take a value of .46. This agreement occurs because the mean square for variation among the authors (or k means) differs only slightly from the interaction mean square in Table 6; when these two sources of variation are pooled in the example above, the value of R is unaffected (see Chapter IV).

D. THE ESTIMATION OF RELIABILITY: A GENERAL CASE

We have seen that it is not particularly meaningful to speak of a single over-all estimate of the reliability of a given standardized test. The reason is that, in general, two or more sources of variation are present in the measurement situation which is used to obtain the estimate of test reliability. Thus the assumption that the observed score, x, is the sum of two components—the hypothetical "true" score, $\tilde{T}$, and the difference between it and the observed score or the error of measurement, e—is an oversimplification of the problem. Rather, it will be necessary to consider several relevant e's or sources of variation in estimating coefficients of test reliability. In so doing we shall find that a meaningful R can be defined which corresponds to each of the definitions of test reliability.

Standardized objective tests are used in a wide variety of situations to characterize the skills, abilities, or other attributes of individuals. But from a practical point of view we are interested in knowing how accurately a given test score describes a given individual. The accuracy of such a description is decreased as a result of unaccountable variations (i.e., e's) in the individual's score, which can arise from three potential sources.

One of these sources (*item inconsistency*) is the error incurred in the construction of the test, which involves the faulty sampling of test units so that they are not representative of the abilities presumably being measured.

The second source of error (*individual variability*) lies in variations in the state of motivation or alertness of the individual when he takes the test. Clearly, if the test is repeated, his scores on each test unit will vary because his efficiency in responding to the test varies from hour to hour, day to day, month to month, and so on. This variability should be looked upon as a property of the individual (not as a property of the test) which will influence the scores on repeated occasions, regardless of how accurately the test is made.

A third source of error (*true test error*) arises when the individual is not able to answer each item with equal certainty, or may resort to guessing when he does not know the correct answer, or may accidentally misread or confuse instructions or items in the test. True-false and multiple-choice tests are particularly sensitive to chance variations because of guessing. The expected effect of the error due to guessing can be removed by suitable corrections, but the variation due to guessing or similar errors cannot be eliminated. The last source of variation is truly a characteristic of the test and can be reduced, just as the variation due to unrepresentative sampling of the test units can be reduced, by increasing the length of the test.

Most of the conventional indices of test reliability oversimplify the problem by ignoring or confounding these three separate components of variation in the estimate of reliability. For example, an index of test reliability based on *parallel forms* given on different occasions confounds variation which is due to sampling of test items, to variability within individuals, and to true test error. If the parallel forms have been constructed by careful matching of items, the component due to sampling test items may be small, in which case estimates of reliability based on parallel tests measure individual variability plus true error simultaneously. Since both of these sources of error enter into the error which affects the accuracy of assigning a score to a given individual, this method of test reliability reflects best the variation which is relevant in the measurement of individual differences. The variation measured by the method of parallel forms will be somewhat dependent on the length of time that intervenes between the administration of the first and second forms. This period must not be so long that it picks up important changes in the individuals who take the test, but it must be long enough to measure short-run variability which is of no interest. Finally, this method does not give any real estimate of the true error of the test unless, of course, variability within individuals is negligible (see formula 9 below).

The second method of estimating test reliability is to *repeat the same test* on subsequent occasions. This method assesses the true error of the test plus the error due to variation within individuals, but it does not assess variation due to the sampling of test items. Since repeating the same test can be thought of as administering two perfectly parallel forms, this method will give results similar to the parallel-forms method in so far as the two forms have been made equivalent. In practice, however, if the same form is used to obtain a measure of test-retest reliability, the coefficient will tend to be somewhat higher than if two parallel forms are used to obtain a test-retest measure of reliability. This difference occurs partly because there is no variation due to sampling of test items when the same test is repeated, and also because the second administration of the same form to the same individuals does not yield truly independent scores. The latter effect can be reduced by extending the period of time between administration of the two forms and by making the number of items so great that the subjects will not remember how they responded on the first administration (see formula **10** below).

Test reliability may also be estimated by the *split-half* method, or its generalization in the Kuder-Richardson (1937) formula 20, which yields a measure of the internal consistency of a test. As will be seen in Table 7, this reliability coefficient measures simultaneously the true error of the test and any possible interaction between the individuals taking the test and the types of items in the test. If it can be assumed that this interaction is negligible (i.e., that the test items are completely homogeneous), this reliability coefficient measures the true error of the test. It may be questioned, however, whether the above-mentioned interaction is zero or negligible over a variety of testing conditions, so that this measure more properly should be regarded as the lower bound for the reliability based on the true error of the test. The source of variation due to the individual-item interaction can be made almost as small as desired by increasing the length of the test, which has the effect of reducing the chance error and also the inhomogeneity due to the sampling of test items (see formula **11** below).

With the proper experimental design it is possible to estimate the components of variance due to each of the three sources of variation mentioned above and to their interactions. But, since there are three sources of random variation, a random analysis of variance model involving a three-way classification is required as follows: Suppose i individuals are given j test units on each of k occasions. We shall assume that the test is long enough that the individuals will not remember their responses from one administration of the test to the next and that if there are any systematic learning effects they are the same for all individuals. As for the two-way model discussed in Chapter V, we assume that the components of a given score, x, of the ith individual for the jth test unit on the kth replication are additive. In this context the components of the score x_{ijk} are, of course, the hypothetical "true" score, $\tilde{T}$, each of the three random components, and their interactions. Consequently,

$$x_{ijk} = \tilde{T} + e_i + e_j + e_k + e_{ij} + e_{ik} + e_{jk} + e_{ijk}$$

Again let us assume that the deviations of the components about $\tilde{T}$ are normally and independently distributed with a mean of zero and their respective variances. We can then specify the components of variance associated with each of the random components of each score by the following notations:

$$\sigma_{x_{ijk}}{}^2 = \sigma_i{}^2 + \sigma_j{}^2 + \sigma_k{}^2 + \sigma_{ij}{}^2 + \sigma_{ik}{}^2 + \sigma_{jk}{}^2 + \sigma_{ijk}{}^2$$

The general three-way classification analysis of variance model is given in Table 7.

We shall use the random three-way model to obtain several general estimates of test reliability. This being the case, the finite population correction will take the value of 1 and hence can be ignored for the time being. But in the estimation of reliability the number of test units per cell will be 1, so that $s = 1$. We have seen that, when $s = 1$, an estimate of $\sigma_e{}^2$ based on within-cell variation is not available, and we shall have to use V_{ijk} as the estimate of the error term. In so doing we shall assume that $\sigma_{ijk}{}^2 = 0$, so that $\sigma_e{}^2 + \sigma_{ijk}{}^2 = \sigma_e{}^2$. Although this assumption is usually tenable, it should be noted that it is made here out of necessity rather than out of choice.

The *test units* are defined in the same manner as the experimental units referred to in Chapter V; hence the test unit can be regarded as the smallest unit of test material which is scored and analyzed as such. The test unit can be defined as the total score on a test, the score on half of the test, a block of items, or an individual item, depending on the method used to estimate test reliability (e.g., the test-retest, split-half, or Kuder-Richardson method). In making the following estimates of test reliability it is assumed that the means of the test units will not differ and that there will be no over-all gain as a result of test replication. If such differences in fact do occur, their presence will not be reflected in the following R's used to estimate test reliability.

We have seen that R may be estimated as a ratio of the

TABLE 7
General Three-Way Analysis of Variance Model

Source of Variation	df	MS†	E(MS)
Individuals (I)	$(i-1)$	V_i	$\sigma_e^2 + \left(\dfrac{J-j}{J}\right)\left(\dfrac{K-k}{K}\right)s\sigma_{ijk}^2 + \left(\dfrac{K-k}{K}\right)sj\sigma_{ik}^2 + \left(\dfrac{J-j}{J}\right)sk\sigma_{ij}^2 + sjk\sigma_i^2$
Test units (J)	$(j-1)$	V_j	$\sigma_e^2 + \left(\dfrac{I-i}{I}\right)\left(\dfrac{K-k}{K}\right)s\sigma_{ijk}^2 + \left(\dfrac{K-k}{K}\right)si\sigma_{jk}^2 + \left(\dfrac{I-i}{I}\right)sk\sigma_{ij}^2 + sik\sigma_j^2$
Replications (K)	$(k-1)$	V_k	$\sigma_e^2 + \left(\dfrac{I-i}{I}\right)\left(\dfrac{J-j}{J}\right)s\sigma_{ijk}^2 + \left(\dfrac{J-j}{J}\right)si\sigma_{jk}^2 + \left(\dfrac{I-i}{I}\right)sj\sigma_{ik}^2 + sij\sigma_k^2$
Test units × individuals (IJ)	$(i-1)(j-1)$	V_{ij}	$\sigma_e^2 + \left(\dfrac{K-k}{K}\right)s\sigma_{ijk}^2 + sk\sigma_{ij}^2$
Individuals × replications (IK)	$(i-1)(k-1)$	V_{ik}	$\sigma_e^2 + \left(\dfrac{J-j}{J}\right)s\sigma_{ijk}^2 + sj\sigma_{ik}^2$
Test units × replications (JK)	$(j-1)(k-1)$	V_{jk}	$\sigma_e^2 + \left(\dfrac{I-i}{I}\right)s\sigma_{ijk}^2 + si\sigma_{jk}^2$
Individuals × test units × replications (IJK)	$(i-1)(j-1)(k-1)$	V_{ijk}	$\sigma_e^2 + s\sigma_{ijk}^2$
Residual (within cells) (e)	$ijk(s-1)$	V_e	σ_e^2

† The symbol V is used as a simplified abbreviation for the respective mean squares.

appropriate components of variance. The respective components of variance for Table 7 are estimated by the same rule that was used in connection with Table 4. Specifically, since $s = 1$ and we are not otherwise interested in σ_{ijk}^2:

$$\sigma_e^2 \doteq V_{ijk}$$

$$\sigma_{jk}^2 \doteq \frac{V_{jk} - V_{ijk}}{i}$$

$$\sigma_{ik}^2 \doteq \frac{V_{ik} - V_{ijk}}{j}$$

$$\sigma_{ij}^2 \doteq \frac{V_{ij} - V_{ijk}}{k}$$

$$\sigma_k^2 \doteq \frac{V_k - V_{ik} - V_{jk} + V_{ijk}}{ij}$$

$$\sigma_j^2 \doteq \frac{V_j - V_{ij} - V_{jk} + V_{ijk}}{ik}$$

$$\sigma_i^2 \doteq \frac{V_i - V_{ik} - V_{ij} + V_{ijk}}{jk}$$

From the appropriate components of variance (or the mean squares), we can now estimate four measures of test reliability and observe the relations among them, as follows:

Coefficient of test unit equivalence (parallel-form reliability):

$$R_E = \frac{\sigma_i^2}{\sigma_i^2 + \sigma_{ij}^2 + \sigma_{ik}^2 + \sigma_e^2}$$

$$\doteq \frac{V_i - V_{ij} - V_{ik} + V_{ijk}}{V_i + (j-1)V_{ij} + (k-1)V_{ik} + (j-1)(k-1)V_{ijk}} \quad [9$$

Coefficient of test unit stability (test-retest reliability):

$$R_S = \frac{\sigma_i^2}{\sigma_i^2 + \sigma_{ik}^2 + \sigma_e^2}$$

$$\doteq \frac{V_i - V_{ij} - V_{ik} + V_{ijk}}{V_i - V_{ij} + (k-1)V_{ik} + (jk - k + 1)V_{ijk}} \quad [10$$

(Note: If $\sigma_{ij}^2 = 0$, $R_E = R_S$; otherwise $R_S > R_E$)

Coefficient of test unit consistency:

$$R_C = \frac{\sigma_i^2}{\sigma_i^2 + \sigma_{ij}^2 + \sigma_e^2}$$

11] $\doteq \dfrac{V_i - V_{ij} - V_{ik} + V_{ijk}}{V_i + (j-1)V_{ij} - V_{ik} + (jk - k + 1)V_{ijk}}$

Coefficient of true test unit reliability:

12] $R_T = \dfrac{\sigma_i^2}{\sigma_i^2 + \sigma_e^2} \doteq \dfrac{V_i - V_{ij} - V_{ik} + V_{ijk}}{V_i - V_{ij} - V_{ik} + (jk + 1)V_{ijk}}$

(Note: If $\sigma_{ij}^2 = 0$ for R_C, $R_C = R_T$; otherwise $R_T > R_C$.)

One may ask whether it is possible to determine the F's which correspond to R_E, R_S, R_C, and R_T based on a three-way random model in order to determine their P-values or, more important, their confidence limits. The answer is that it is not possible to determine these F's directly in the random model, since there are no simple effects or interactions whose $E(MS)$ are the same as those of the F's which correspond to R_E, R_S, R_C, and R_T. The general rule is that the numerator of F contains all the variance components with their coefficients that make up the $E(MS)$ for the effect or interaction to be tested, whereas the denominator of F contains all the same components and their coefficients except for the one component and its coefficients associated with the effect or interaction to be tested (see Tables 4 and 5). On examination of Table 7 it will be apparent that this rule cannot be applied directly to estimate the F's which correspond to the above R's—which will almost certainly be statistically significant anyway (see also Section E below).

The components of variance for certain interaction terms in R_E, R_S, R_C, and R_T are, however, of both theoretical and practical importance. Specifically, the difference between R_E and R_S and between R_C and R_T rests on whether σ_{ij}^2 is greater than 0. Similarly the difference between the first two and the second two R's rests on whether the interaction component σ_{ik}^2 is greater than 0. We have seen how it is possible to determine the size of these estimated components of variance, and it is also apparent from Table 7 that their corresponding F-values can be estimated. Specifically, the test for

$\sigma_{ij}{}^2$ is $F = V_{ij}/V_{ijk}$, and the test for $\sigma_{ik}{}^2$ is $F = V_{ik}/V_{ijk}$, with their corresponding *df*.

There is another important distinction between the first two and the second two formulas for estimating reliability coefficients. The distinction lies in the fact that formulas **9** and **10** usually would be applied to total test scores as the test units, whereas formulas **11** and **12** usually would be applied to the individual items as the test units. It will therefore be necessary to adjust the latter coefficients if they are to be made comparable to customary estimates of test reliability, which are always concerned with the reliability of the total test score, even though it may be estimated from the reliability of items. (Actually, formula **9** and **10** should be adjusted also if they are based on test units which are $1/j^{th}$ of the total test score.)

The proper method for adjusting R_C and R_T is to apply the Spearman-Brown prophecy formula in terms of the number of test items or units used in estimating R_C and R_T as reliability coefficients. (The R's thus adjusted will be marked with an asterisk.) Consequently, if *j* units are involved,

$$R_{jj} = \frac{jR}{1 + (j - 1)R}$$

But, when R_C is thus entered into the Spearman-Brown formula, the resulting coefficient becomes equivalent to the Kuder-Richardson (1937) formula 20. That is to say,

$$R_C{}^* = R_{K-R} = \frac{jR_C}{1 + (j - 1)R_C} \qquad [13$$

Similarly,

$$R_T{}^* = \frac{jR_T}{1 + (j - 1)R_T} \qquad [14$$

It is instructive to consider the difference between $R_C{}^*$ or R_{K-R} and $R_T{}^*$. From the formulas for R_C and R_T we saw that these two estimates differ in so far as the component of variance $\sigma_{ij}{}^2$ is involved in the estimation of R_C but is not involved in the estimation of R_T. Stated differently, $R_C = R_T$ when the test items are completely homogeneous so that no individual-test unit interaction exists; that is, when $\sigma_{ij}{}^2 = 0$.

The question whether the component $\sigma_{ij}{}^2$ should or should not be present in the estimation of the coefficient measuring the consistency of a test can be answered in terms of the $E(MS)$ given in Table 7. Let us consider two conditions or assumptions: (*i*) the test units (*j*'s) are random, being sampled randomly from a very large universe of such test items, and (*ii*) the test units are fixed, in the sense that the reliability of a test is estimated in terms of *a fixed number of items and only those items*. Needless to say, the individuals (*i*'s) are always considered randomly sampled, so that the estimated reliability coefficient may be applicable to other persons who presumably will be drawn from the same population. (In this type of situation the test is given only once, so that replications—*k*'s—do not exist.)

(*i*) If the test items can be considered randomly sampled from a very large number of such items and are not just a specified set of items, it is seen from Table 7 that the $E(MS)$ for individuals will be: $\sigma_e{}^2 + \sigma_{ij}{}^2 + j\sigma_i{}^2$. Consequently $\sigma_{ij}{}^2$ is a component of random variation and should appear in the measure of reliability. For this case $R_C{}^*$, or the regular Kuder-Richardson formula 20, is the proper index, and it measures simultaneously the true internal test error, $\sigma_e{}^2$, and the error due to sampling test items, $\sigma_{ij}{}^2$.[4] It is thus to be expected that, as the number of items is increased, the size of the component $\sigma_{ij}{}^2$ will decrease, and theoretically would vanish if an infinite number of items were sampled.

(*ii*) If the test items are fixed (as they more frequently are), the $E(MS)$ for individuals will be $\sigma_e{}^2 + j\sigma_i{}^2$, and the measure of reliability should reflect only the true internal test error, $\sigma_e{}^2$. With reference to the use of the Kuder-Richardson formula, it has frequently been observed that "if the items in a test cover many different abilities, the estimate from this formula is low, sometimes much too low" (Cronbach, 1949, pp. 66–69). This observation applies, of course, only when the items are fixed; when the items are randomly selected this estimate of reliability is not "too low"; it is the proper estimate. If the Kuder-Richardson formula is used, $\sigma_{ij}{}^2$ is always present and

---

[4] The component $\sigma_{ij}{}^2$ is Lord's (1955) type-2 sampling variance, although he arrived at his result on the basis of other considerations.

inseparable from the component for true test error, σ_e^2. If, however, it can be assumed that there is no interaction between individuals and test items, which occurs when the items are completely homogeneous, the Kuder-Richardson formula will equal the measure for true internal error, R_T^*.[5] If such interaction exists (that is, $\sigma_{ij}^2 > 0$), a split-half formula based on matched items will most closely approximate R_T^*. If the component σ_{ij}^2 is known to be greater than 0 when the test units are fixed, and if one wishes an estimate of reliability based only on the "true test error," σ_e^2, it is clear that the formula for R_T^* should be used—not the formula for R_C^* or R_{K-R}.

When the reliability coefficients R_E, R_S, R_C, or R_T are estimated from individual items or other test units of equal size and adjusted so as to be comparable to estimates based on the total test score, the term "unit" should be dropped in designating these coefficients. Under these conditions they should be called the coefficients of *test equivalence*, *test stability*, *test consistency*, and *true test reliability*.

The purpose of this section has been to discuss the logic of reliability estimation and to suggest a general approach to this type of research question. The computational procedures for obtaining the mean squares (V's) necessary to compute formulas **9** to **12** are the same as those used in connection with any three-way factorial design.

(Incidentally, it is questionable whether certain assumptions underlying the analysis of variance are met in the limiting case in which the test units can be scored only according to a two-point scale. Specifically, with respect to the "normality" of the distribution, it is questionable whether one can assume that true-false responses are normally distributed, so that some uncertainty exists with respect to the interpretation of the F's and R's based on such data. This question does not apply to nearly the same degree when the test units are single multiple-choice items or blocks of true-false items.)

---

[5] There are various lines of evidence which indicate that on many tests not all persons respond identically to all test items under all conditions (cf. Haggard, 1954). Furthermore, in the following chapter the method used in the analysis of differences among profiles of scores rests on the fact that the interaction designated here as σ_{ij}^2 is greater than 0.

It may be noted that a variety of other approaches to the problem of estimating test consistency has been suggested (e.g., Hoyt, 1941). We may, for example, consider that the test items are homogeneous in the sense that they all measure a single general factor, so that all the items measure the "same thing." From this point of view we would approach the problem in terms of the self-correlation among the items or the reliability of the means of the scores of each individual. Similarly the distinction between reliability estimates based on items which are assumed to be either (*i*) random or (*ii*) fixed can also be arrived at by an examination of Tables 4 and 5 for the two-way classification in which the estimate of σ_e^2 is based on replications (i.e., $s>1$). Let us consider classification C to be individuals and classification K to be test units; since C will be random in either case, the R for K random will be

$$\frac{\sigma_c^2}{\sigma_c^2 + \sigma_{ck}^2 + \sigma_e^2} = R_C$$

and the R for K fixed will be

$$\frac{\sigma_c^2}{\sigma_c^2 + \sigma_e^2} = R_T$$

These coefficients may then be adjusted by the Spearman-Brown formula as before. It can also be shown that the Kuder-Richardson estimate of reliability can be obtained from the F's which correspond to these R's by the general formula

15] $$R_{K-R} = 1 - \frac{1}{F} = 1 - \frac{R'MS}{BCMS} = R_C^*$$

These various approaches to the estimation of test consistency (or reliability of the means) are essentially the same. Their equality may be seen in the manner in which the appropriate components of variance enter into their estimation.[6]

It should be noted that, in practice, the above formulas for

---

[6] For other general discussions of test reliability see, for example, Jackson, 1939; Ferguson, 1941; Jackson and Ferguson, 1941; Guttman, 1945; Cronbach, 1947; Loevinger, 1947; Horst, 1949; Gulliksen, 1950; Cronbach, 1951; Thorndike *et al.*, 1951; Lindquist, 1953; Burt, 1955; Mahmoud, 1955; and Tryon, 1957.

estimating reliability coefficients will not apply in connection with all research problems, since the applicability of any formula will depend on the nature of the model that is appropriate in the analysis of any particular set of data. Not all situations are sufficiently complex to justify the use of the formulas given in this section. For example, suppose that an investigator has available several persons who wish to serve as judges in a long-range research project, and he has to select the three judges which are the most "reliable" raters of projective test protocols, where reliability is used in the sense of stability of rating particular variables. Suppose also that the investigator has selected twenty-five representative TAT protocols and has decided to have each of the potential judges rate each protocol on a measure of over-all adjustment on five occasions one month apart.

In this example the protocols and occasions are fixed for each rater, so that there is only one source of random variation, namely, variation in the judgment of the raters in assigning scores to each protocol over the five occasions. Consequently, in computing the reliability coefficient for each rater, the appropriate model is a 1 (rater) $\times$ 25 (protocols or classes) design with $s = 5$ (ratings) per cell. It will be seen that this example is identical with the one given at the end of Section C of this chapter, where σ_c^2 is estimated from the variation between the twenty-five protocols (classes) and σ_{wc}^2 is estimated from the variation within classes, and $R = \sigma_c^2/(\sigma_c^2 + \sigma_{wc}^2)$ (see also Bock, 1956). The investigator, after computing the R's for each rater, could then select the three persons who show the greatest degree of stability in rating the twenty-five protocols. (It is apparent, of course, that this criterion of reliability does not bear on such questions as the degree of accuracy or validity of the ratings.)

E. THE POSSIBLE THREE-WAY FACTORIAL MODELS

Table 7 can be used as a general guide for determining any factorial three-way classification model in the same manner as Table 5 was derived from Table 4 for the two-way classification models. By an examination of these tables it is possible to clarify certain important similarities and differences between F and R. That is to say, when the corresponding F's and R's are available, R differs from F in that R can be expressed as the ratio of a single component of variance to all of the same components of variance that enter the numerator of the corresponding F. The coefficients which accompany the components of variance cancel out in this expression of R; they do not cancel out for the corresponding F. (This difference, incidentally, shows why the statistic R has relatively uniform meaning and an upper limit of $+1$ whereas the presence of the coefficients in the formula for the test-static, F, precludes such uniformity.)

As an illustration of Table 7, let us suppose that classification K is fixed at some specified value (i.e., $K = k$), with classifications I and J random. In this mixed model, if $s = 1$, the $E(MS)$ for I is $\sigma_e^2 + k\sigma_{ij}^2 + jk\sigma_i^2$. In the particular case where $k = 1$, the design reduces to a two-way model and it is readily possible to estimate the F which corresponds to R_C. The test is

$$16]\qquad F = \frac{\sigma_e^2 + \sigma_{ij}^2 + j\sigma_i^2}{\sigma_e^2 + \sigma_{ij}^2} \doteq \frac{V_i}{V_{ij}}$$

with the *df* for V_i and V_{ij}.

In more general applications of Table 7 to the various factorial designs used in experimentation, it is to be expected that, in the large majority of cases, two or more experimental units will be entered into each *ijk* classification or cell. In such cases, $s \geqslant 2$ and the $E(MS)$ for each classification will be altered, as σ_e^2 will be estimated on the basis of the variation of scores within cells (rather than by using σ_{ijk}^2 as the estimate of σ_e^2 when $s = 1$), and the remaining components of variance in the $E(MS)$ will take the coefficient s. Let us return to the example above where I and J are random and K is fixed. Let us further assume that I (3 levels) and J (4 levels) are random and K (2 levels) is fixed, and $s = 5$. The $E(MS)$ for classification I will then be

$$\sigma_e^2 + sk\sigma_{ij}^2 + sjk\sigma_i^2 = \sigma_e^2 + (5 \times 2)\sigma_{ij}^2 + (5 \times 4 \times 2)\sigma_i^2.$$

Because K is fixed, the components for σ_{ijk}^2 and σ_{ik}^2 drop out of the $E(MS)$ for classification I. The $E(MS)$ for the J and K classifications and for the IJ, IK, and JK interactions can likewise be written by following Table 7. Furthermore, if any of the classifications is sampled from a small finite population, it is possible to apply the *fpc* and estimate the proper $E(MS)$ in each case (see pp. 62–67). Thus, whether the fixed, the random, or any of the six mixed three-way factorial models are used, one can determine the $E(MS)$ and hence the appropriate F's and R's from Table 7 without ambiguity.

It should be emphasized that one cannot generalize routinely from the F's and R's appropriate for the two-way model (as indicated in Tables 4 and 5) when one is actually working with the three-way model. Similarities do, of course, exist, as in the case of the fixed model where σ_e^2 is the proper error term in testing each of the main effects and interactions. But when random classifications are involved it is frequently not possible to make an exact test of certain main effects, as an examination of Table 7 will indicate. Exact tests cannot be made when meaningful F ratios cannot be formed in terms of the $E(MS)$. That is to say, the denominator of the F ratio must contain all the components of variance and their coefficients which also appear in the numerator of the F ratio—except for the component and its coefficients being tested. Thus, for example, none of the main effects can be tested directly in the random three-way model. But in this case, where each of the three classifications is random, it is seldom of real interest to know the "significance" of these main effects; rather, certain interactions and their magnitude generally are of interest and may be tested. If direct tests of certain effects are not possible, and if the investigator should desire to test such effects, he may wish to use approximate F-tests.[7]

---

[7] Alternate (or approximate) F-tests and methods for determining the *df* have been suggested for these cases (cf. Satterthwaite, 1946; Cochran, 1951). Summaries of alternate F-tests when direct tests are not available are given in Anderson and Bancroft (1952, Ch. 23) and Harter and Lum (1955, pp. 17–20).

VII

the application of intraclass correlation to pattern analytic studies

A. INTRODUCTION

The research questions usually subsumed under the heading of reliability are answered by data in the form of single scores, each of the same kind, from a number of individuals. Even when repeated measures are taken, they are still single scores (such as the total number of items correct) of the same kind as those recorded initially. Consequently the procedures for estimating reliability are not of much use to the investigator who is faced with the problem of analyzing sets or profiles of scores, all more or less different from one another, from a number of individuals, or several repetitions of the set of scores from one individual. And, because many behavioral scientists believe that the complexities of man's behavior cannot be expressed by a single score, they have devised tests which provide several measures at the same time. It is thus highly desirable that appropriate statistical techniques be made available to research workers and practitioners who use such tests. A variety of pattern analytic methods has been suggested.[1]

Any method which purports to analyze a set of scores at one time should possess certain properties. First of all, it should enable the investigator to answer certain crucial questions about his data, and it should also provide an estimate of the standard error, so that he can estimate the precision, stability, or significance of his findings. The method should also be practicable and understandable to the majority of research workers so that they will be able to use it in their work. At first glance, it would appear that the coefficient of intraclass correlation might be used to analyze sets of scores, since many aspects of the problem of pattern analysis are concerned essentially with questions of intersubject agreement and intrasubject stability.

But, before proceeding to discuss this possibility, it is necessary first to specify the manner in which the terms profile and pattern will be used, since these terms have often been applied synonymously in the description of both individuals and groups of individuals.

B. DEFINITIONS OF PROFILES AND PATTERNS

In the following discussion the word *profile* will be used to denote a particular configuration of the scores of an individual on a fixed set of variables comprising a battery of tests. It is here assumed that each configuration connotes some unique meaning and that, if the scores were changed, the new configuration would have a different meaning. Thus for a given battery of tests there is assumed to exist for every individual a profile which describes him in some manner. Generalizing the concept of profile to a group of individuals, the word *pattern* will be reserved to describe a set of profiles.

---

[1] Short of multivariate methods (e.g., Rao, 1952), several persons have proposed pattern analytic techniques, such as: Zubin, 1937; Ellson, 1947; Cattell, 1949; du Mas, 1949; Meehl, 1950; Block, Levine and McNemar, 1951; Osgood and Suci, 1952; Webster, 1952; Cronbach and Gleser, 1953; Gaier and Lee, 1953; Horst, 1954; Mosel and Roberts, 1954; Danford, 1955; Tiedeman, 1955; Lykken, 1956; McQuitty, 1956; and Haggard and Chapman.

A pattern may approach one of several ideal forms in the limiting cases. If all the individuals constituting the group have the same score on each test, and therefore have identical profiles, the set will be called a *congruent pattern*. If the scores on the various tests differ by at most a constant, and thus give profiles which differ at most in level, the set will be called a *parallel pattern*. But, if the profiles constituting the pattern overlap, as in the case of a random collection of profiles, so that the conditions of identity or of similarity no longer exist, the set will be called a *mixed pattern*. Finally, when a set of profiles is maximally dissimilar (in the sense that R takes its minimal value), the set will be called an *incongruent pattern*.

The essence of a pattern is thus the relative position, both in level and in direction, of the scores in one profile as compared to those in the rest of the set. It may be observed here that the conventional use of the term pattern is confined to the cases here called congruent or parallel, and in that sense the mixed and incongruent cases are not considered patterns at all. Although congruent or parallel patterns are generally of greater interest, one may wish to form and study groups of dissimilar or heterogeneous individuals; then it is desirable to form mixed or incongruent patterns based on profile scores. The distinction here brought out may be justified on the ground that in the ideal case, as we shall see later, $R_P = 1$ for the congruent pattern, as well as for the parallel pattern if the differences in profile levels (or k means) are partialed out; whereas for a mixed pattern R_P does not differ from 0 and, when an incongruent pattern exists, $R_P = -1/(k - 1)$ (see Chapter V, Special Cases 1 and 2). There will, of course, almost always be some departures from these ideal values.

In addition to any formal definitions of patterns, however, the composition of a pattern may be defined in one of several ways. For example, theoretical a priori patterns may be defined in some cases where a clearly formulated theory requires that persons belonging to a particular pattern must have high scores on one measure, low scores on another, and so on. Where such specifications can be clearly defined, only those persons who receive such a profile of scores can be said to belong to that pattern. Empirical a priori patterns may also be defined on the basis of findings from previous researches as, for example, when an investigator has come to expect that, under specified conditions, successful pilots will score high on "ability to relax," low on "distractability under stress," and so on. In addition, patterns may be defined in terms of various external or behavioral criteria, in which case it is assumed that a relation exists between such criteria and the measures included in the test battery.

If theoretical a priori definitions, or expectations based on previous findings, or outside behavioral criteria are not available, one is forced to rely on some form of empirical-statistical definition of a pattern. By and large, meaningful statistical definitions of patterns may be accomplished by multivariate methods of analysis of profiles; but this topic is beyond the scope of this discussion. Possible safeguards against the risks inherent in an arbitrary empirical-statistical definition of a pattern lie in relating it to some broader context of knowledge and in determining its stability by appropriate tests of significance. Under conditions to be specified, when R is statistically significant one may assume that the profiles which compose the pattern are sufficiently alike to warrant using the means of the scores in each class (i.e., a profile based on the class means) as a stable operational criterion to define the pattern.

C. THE NATURE OF THE STATISTICAL PROBLEM

In the preceding chapters we have seen that estimates of the coefficient of intraclass correlation can be obtained from specific analysis of variance designs. It is important to note that all these designs were limited to a *single* variable; that is, the data represented measures on a single trait, characteristic, or attribute of each individual. Specifically, the scores represented an academic achievement score, the I.Q. of members of friendship pairs, a measure of hand strength, or other single experimental or test units. This type of analysis of variance design, which is commonly used in educational and psychological statistics, has been taken directly from methods developed for agronomists who are concerned with differences on a single variable, namely, yield of crop, under the influence of different treatments or conditions, such as types of fertilizers or soils.

In the behavioral sciences, however, much of the investigator's work cannot reasonably be limited to the study of a single variable. For example, many psychological tests are purposely designed to yield a set of scores, no single one of which can be meaningfully interpreted in isolation from the others. Or, in clinical practice, one may wish to classify patients for therapy on the basis of scores from several types of assessments. Or, in studies of academic achievement one may wish to study the influence of various conditions on the performance of individuals in several academic subjects simultaneously, and so on. In all such cases where a *set of related scores* may be involved, the data cannot be analyzed appropriately by the methods of univariate statistics. Rather this type of data can be analyzed rigorously only by methods of multivariate statistics, such as discriminant analysis and the analysis of dispersion.

Although the multivariate methods demand a knowledge of mathematics which puts them beyond the scope of any introductory text in statistics, it must be emphasized that there are no alternatives to these methods if full rigor is required. Yet many research workers to whom the multivariate statistical methods are not available would benefit if a technique no more complex than the analysis of variance could be used to abstract out a large part of the information inherent in multivariate data. It is the purpose of this chapter to propose such a technique—in particular, the use of R and F as a means of characterizing and testing the similarity of sets of scores derived from standardized tests.

In appraising any method which intends to utilize the analysis of variance technique to make statistical inferences, it is useful to recall the assumptions which must be met (or approximated) if the use of the technique is to be justified. These assumptions, which were summarized briefly in Chapter V, require that the data to be analyzed be in a form such that *the various sources of variation are additive, and that the random errors are normally distributed, are uncorrelated among themselves, and have a common variance.* We shall consider some of the characteristics of scores from standardized test batteries and the rationale for meeting (or approximating) the above assumptions in order to use R as a measure of similarity of the profiles and to determine the extent to which they form particular patterns.

An appreciation of the specific meaning of these assumptions in the context of pattern analytic studies can best be seen by considering the analysis of variance model that we shall need to use. In general terms, we wish to arrange the scores in a $c \times k$ matrix, with c subtest scores for k individuals (or perhaps c subtest scores for one individual who, over time, gives k scores for each subtest). In this two-way model it is clear that a specified and constant set of subtests will be used, so that the c levels of C will be fixed. We can, however, consider the k levels of K to be either random or fixed, since we can select at random the profiles of k individuals from a large population of such individuals, or we can choose to study the profiles of k particular individuals, or the profiles of one individual over k trials. In either case, the units will be single scores on the c subtests (i.e., $s = 1$) in this model.

We are faced with several difficulties in connection with the above model, regardless of whether K is random or fixed. For one thing, the estimate of σ_e^2 is based on the *variation among the randomly sampled units within a cell*. And, since any subtest score or unit can appear in only one cell, it will not be possible to use the responses of an individual to all the c subtests to estimate σ_e^2. When k individuals are involved, one solution to the problem would be to have each of them take the test battery two or more times; then the σ_e^2 could be estimated from the two or more units in each cell. Unfortunately, this solution is not practicable in most cases.

If we assume that K is random (i.e., $K = \infty$ in the population), so that the $c \times k$ model above is mixed, we run into difficulty because tests of the type we are considering are so standardized that $BCMS = 0$ when $K = \infty$ in the population. Consequently, as we have seen in Chapter V, Special Case 3, it would be necessary to use the interaction term, or IMS, to estimate the F which corresponds to R as a measure of similarity or dissimilarity among profiles of subtest scores. But from Tables 4 and 5 it is clear that in this two-way mixed model σ_e^2 is required in order to estimate R and F based on IMS. Furthermore, if we assume that K is fixed, so that the $c \times k$ model above is fixed, we likewise find that an estimate of σ_e^2 is required to estimate the appropriate R and F. Thus, in pattern analytic studies of the type we are considering, the analysis of variance technique cannot be applied directly to the subtest scores provided by standardized test batteries because, when $s = 1$, it is not possible to obtain an estimate of σ_e^2 from the data itself.

D. A PROPOSED METHOD FOR USING R IN PATTERN ANALYTIC STUDIES

Since the error estimate, σ_e^2, is properly based on the sampling of test units (the subtest scores), the only meaningful method of sampling such units is in terms of repeated testings over time. In order to provide a method by which the analysis of variance technique can be used in pattern analytic studies, it will be necessary first to obtain an estimate of σ_e^2 which has the following properties: (1) the errors are normally distributed and uncorrelated over time and (2) the errors are homogeneous within individuals. We shall consider each of these properties of σ_e^2 in turn.

1. errors which are normally and independently distributed (uncorrelated)

The proposed method makes important use of the fact that, if a number of tests are given to one individual on repeated occasions, the intercorrelations among the scores on the same variable over repetitions can generally be assumed to be insignificantly small, provided, of course, that any systematic increments (or other order effects) due to such factors as practice have been removed. Thus, if we (*i*) give a series of parallel tests to a group of individuals and adjust the scores so that the mean for all individuals is constant from one occasion to another, then (*ii*) compute sums of squares and cross-products for each individual corrected to his mean score for all occasions, then (*iii*) pool these corrected sums of squares and cross-products, and from them (*iv*) compute correlations among the tests *within* individuals and *over* occasions, we will generally find that such correlations are trivially small (cf. Bock and Haggard). This occurs because differences in scores within individuals and over time (after systematic effects have been removed) can be regarded simply as random variations about the mean level for the individual (cf. Ferguson, 1941; Glazer, 1950, 1951; Gulliksen, 1950). If the individual errors are random, the correlations among them over time is zero.

If, then, we wish to determine whether the scores of a number of individuals may be regarded as *not* similar on a set of subtests, we need merely to determine that the differences between individuals are greater than can be attributed to the random variations within individuals. Furthermore, since this variation is uncorrelated from subtest to subtest, its variance may be determined from a pooled estimate based on all the subtests. The following method of pattern analysis and the related significance tests will rest on these assumptions.

2. errors which are homogeneous from unit to unit

We have seen that there is good reason to assume that a characteristic of the response behavior of individuals taking objective tests is that, in general, the errors tend to be random and normally distributed over repetitions for single test units. But, in order to use the analysis of variance technique, we shall have to be able to assume that such random variations are homogeneous over time for a given unit *and* from unit to unit in different subtests.

It is assumed in mental testing theory that the error term for a given subtest will have the same standard deviation (σ_e) over time for all individuals. If this is so, σ_e is equivalent to the "standard error of measurement" of the subtest and may be estimated from the test-retest reliability coefficient (r_{tt}) and the standard deviation (sd_t) of that subtest (see Chapter V, Special Case 2). That is to say, for any subtest, $\sqrt{sd_t^2(1 - r_{tt})}$ provides an estimate of σ_e for that subtest, which, we may assume, is homogeneous over time for individuals.

And, when dealing with all subtests simultaneously, it will be useful to stabilize all the subtest scores so that each subtest has the same variance over temporal repetitions. This may be done by dividing each subtest score by its σ_e, or standard error of measurement. We shall refer to the scores thus obtained as *stabilized scores* (S-scores). S-scores have the advantage that each subtest in the battery contributes equally to the variance of their sum over repeated occasions; that is, $\sigma_{\text{meas.}} = 1$, so that in this case $\sigma_e = \sigma_e^2 = 1$ over repetitions for all subtests and individuals. This estimate of σ_e^2, which is obtained from sources outside the data to be analyzed, will be used to obtain R_{ck} from the analysis of variance table.

If, however, the investigator has obtained repeated measures on the set of subtests from a large number of subjects, the estimate of σ_e^2 based on such repeated scores could be obtained from these data. The square root of this estimate of σ_e^2 could be used to stabilize the scores. Thus, if the investigator has given a standardized test battery to, say, 50 persons at least twice, he could use the estimate of the σ_e^2 to determine whether the profiles of certain members of the group form patterns.

As in Chapter V, let us assume that the components of any stabilized score, z_{cke}, may be written

$$z_{cke} = \tilde{M} + \tilde{M}_c + \tilde{M}_k + \tilde{M}_{ck} + e$$

and that the variance of the z_{cke}'s may be written

$$\sigma_z^2 = (\sigma_c^2) + \sigma_k^2 + \sigma_{ck}^2 + \sigma_e^2$$

(Note that, as before, we are not interested in the value of the over-all mean, $\tilde{M}$, and that the component σ_c^2 is fixed and hence is not properly a component of random variation.)

Using stabilized scores, the two-way analysis of variance table (mixed model with C fixed and K random) may now be written in the following form:

Classification	df	MS	E(MS)
C (subtests)	$(c-1)$	BCMS	$\sigma_e^2 + \left(\dfrac{K-k}{K}\right)\sigma_{ck}^2 + (k\sigma_c^2)$
K (individuals)	$(k-1)$	BKMS	$\sigma_e^2 + \left(\dfrac{C-c}{C}\right)\sigma_{ck}^2 + c\sigma_k^2$
$CK = I$	$(c-1)(k-1)$	IMS	$\sigma_e^2 + \qquad \sigma_{ck}^2$
R' (residual)	$(N \text{ for } r_{tt})$	$(R'MS)$	$\sigma_e^2 = 1$

In making use of the above analysis of variance table we shall not be concerned with actually estimating the components of the stabilized score of a given individual for a given test. We wish, instead, to estimate the respective components of random variation associated with individuals, σ_k^2, and the individual-test interaction, σ_{ck}^2. We shall use these components to define R's which characterize the similarity of the subtest scores of individuals in a given sample in terms of profile and level.

In accordance with the rules discussed in Chapters V and VI we can now determine the appropriate R's, which provide measures of the homogeneity of the profiles in terms of subtest scores and/or levels, and the F's which correspond to them. Specifically,

$$R_P = 1 - R_{ck} = 1 - \frac{IMS - 1}{IMS} = 1 - \frac{\sigma_{ck}^2}{\sigma_{ck}^2 + \sigma_e^2} \qquad [17$$

and

$$R_L = \frac{BKMS - IMS}{BKMS + (k-1)IMS} = \frac{\sigma_k^2}{\sigma_k^2 + \sigma_{ck}^2 + \sigma_e^2} \qquad [18$$

Correspondingly,

$$F_{ck} = \frac{IMS}{1} \qquad [19$$

with $(c-1)(k-1)$ df for the numerator (n_1) and the number of individuals in the sample (N) from which r_{tt} is obtained in the denominator (n_2) of F—if the retest is given once. If the retest is given twice, the df for n_2 will be $2N$, and so on. Similarly,

$$F_k = F_L = \frac{BKMS}{1} \qquad [20$$

It should be noted that in this case the C classification is fixed, with the result that the interaction component drops out of the error term. The df for $F_k = F_L$ will equal $k - 1$ for n_1 with n_2 again determined by the size of the sample used to obtain r_{tt}. For practical purposes, the number of df for n_2 frequently may be considered infinite, particularly when r_{tt} is based on large samples.

E. APPLICATION OF THE METHOD TO PATTERN ANALYTIC STUDIES

In pattern analytic studies the investigator is usually interested in making statements regarding the similarities or differences among sets of scores in terms of both their *profile or pattern* and their *level*. The terms profile and pattern have already been defined in the introduction to this chapter. The term level will be used to designate a measure of the over-all effect of all the subtests taken together.

A meaningful measure of level can be obtained if the intercorrelations among the subtests are all non-negative. If one or more of the subtests correlate negatively with the others in the set, and positively with each other, their scales should be reversed so that all the intercorrelations are positive. If all the subtests are positively intercorrelated, they can be regarded as measuring some general level of performance in relation to some "general factor," which is reflected in the over-all concordance of the test scores of each individual, and the mean of such scores will assess this general level. If this mean is computed from the S-scores, it will be the combination of scores with minimal variance over occasions, and in this sense will be the most efficient estimator of the general level.

The extent to which a set of subtest scores can differentiate among profiles will depend on the measured differences among the individuals tested and on certain properties of the test battery. Thus, if the means of the subtests in the battery are all positively correlated over individuals, the effect of such correlation will be to cut down the ability of the battery to discriminate among patterns of scores based on the subtests. In the limiting case where all the $c(c-1)/2$ inter-subtest r's are $+1$, we would in effect have the equivalent of the score on one subtest, repeated c times. Under these hypothetical conditions any differences among the k profiles presumably would be due to sampling errors. Such a test should, however, differentiate maximally in terms of level. On the other hand, if all the subtest intercorrelations were 0 over individuals, the test would be unable to differentiate in terms of level but would differentiate maximally in terms of pattern.

In practice, we usually find that the subtests tend to be positively correlated in so far as they all measure a common factor. The Wechsler-Bellevue intelligence test (W-B) is a case in point.[2] For this test Wechsler (1944, p. 223) reported inter-subtest r's for normal adults which range from .16 to .72, with a medium r of .46. For any given test these r's may, of course, vary with particular samples or "populations" tested. Data reported for the Minnesota Multiphasic Personality Inventory (MMPI) illustrate this fact. In one study Wheeler *et al.* (1951) reported that for a group of male neuropsychiatric patients the inter-subtest r's (for nine scales)[3] ranged from .04 to .86, with a median r of .46. These authors also report that for a group of male college students the r's for the same scales ranged from .27 to .82, with a median r of .34. Similarly Tyler (1951) reported that for the same tests given to a group of female college graduate students the r's ranged from $-.35$ to .77, with a median r of .19.

Some test batteries were constructed to provide measures which are relatively independent of each other. Edwards (1954*b*), for example, reported that the Personal Preference Schedule, when given to college students, yielded inter-subtest r's which ranged from $-.36$ to .46, with a median r of $-.09$. Other test batteries, however, were constructed so that the subtests correlate among themselves about as much as the behavioral dimensions they attempt to measure correlate in functional social life. This is the rationale used by Gough (1956) in constructing the California Psychological Inventory. Thus we see that the subtest intercorrelations may be expected to vary both

---

[2] I am grateful to Dr. David Wechsler for permission to cite the Wechsler-Bellevue data in Tables 8 and 10. The total Wechsler-Bellevue intelligence scale is made up of five verbal tests (plus an optional vocabulary test) and five performance tests. The raw data for each test are converted into standardized ("weighted") scores, which have a mean of 10 and a sigma of 3. The tests used in the present analysis are: Information, Comprehension, Digit Span, Arithmetic, Similarities, Picture Arrangement, Picture Completion, Block Design, Object Assembly, and Digit Symbol.

[3] The standard MMPI scoring system is made up of four validity scales: Question, Lie, Validity, and K, and nine clinical scales: Hypochondriasis (Hs), Depression (D), Hysteria (Hy), Psychopathic Deviate (Pd), Interest (MF), Paranoia (Pa), Psychasthenia (Pt), Schizophrenia (Sc), and Hypomania (Ma). In later examples we shall use only these nine clinical scales. The raw data for each scale are converted into standardized ("T") scores, which have a mean of 50 and a sigma of 10.

with the relative homogeneity of the individuals who take the test and with the manner in which the test itself was designed and standardized.

F. ILLUSTRATION OF THE METHOD WITH WECHSLER-BELLEVUE DATA

Certain aspects of the analysis of profiles may be illustrated with data provided by Wechsler (1944, pp. 161–166) in his discussion of the diagnostic possibilities of particular configurations of scores on the ten subtests of the W-B intelligence test. He gives the normalized standard scores on a sample of cases from each of the following clinical groups: "organic brain disease," "schizophrenia," "adolescent psychopaths," and "neurotics." If the assumption is true that persons belonging to the same clinical syndrome will have relatively similar scores on the subtests, one would expect high agreement among their profiles, an expectation which should be reflected in a high positive value of R_P.

But, as we have seen, it is necessary to transform the standardized scores into S-scores before proceeding with the analysis of these data. If the investigator has not obtained test-retest data himself, it is necessary to find such data elsewhere. The selection of data (if any are available) from which to estimate the $\sigma_{meas.}$ and hence σ_e^2, rests on the discretion of the investigator. Ordinarily it is to be expected that he will, if possible, select stable data obtained from samples which correspond to his own in terms of age, sex, clinical type, or other variables which might influence the r_{tt} and sd_t. To analyze the profiles provided by Wechsler, we shall utilize the data reported by Derner, Aborn, and Canter (1950). Although we shall be analyzing the profiles of deviate cases, and the data given by Derner *et al.* reflect the performance of "normal" subjects, they are on a relatively large number of cases (158) and provide a composite estimate from separate groups retested after one week, one month, and six months. Consequently it is assumed that these data will provide an estimate of σ_e^2 which is stable and applicable to a wide variety of pattern analytic studies using W-B profiles. See also Wechsler (1955, pp. 5–25).

The data for two of the "neurotics" (N_1, N_2), as transformed to S-scores, are given and analyzed in Table 8, and may be used to test the expectation that these two profiles will be similar. The most apparent difference between the two profiles in Table 8 is in the over-all level scores. The S-scores of 106.60 and 71.09 correspond to a difference of 43 standard score points—or approximately 43 I.Q. points. This difference strongly suggests that the person who contributed to the N_1 profile is the "more intelligent." The F for the level difference between these two profiles is 63.05. This comparison is based on 1 and 158 df and the P-value is less than .01.

TABLE 8
Analysis of Wechsler-Bellevue Scores of
Two Neurotics (N_1, N_2)

Subtests	Standardized Scores = (x)		r_{tt}	sd_t^2	$\sigma_{meas.}$†	Stabilized Scores = $(x/\sigma_{meas.})$		
	N_1	N_2				N_1	N_2	Sum
Verbal tests								
Inf.	14	10	.86	3.30	.68	20.59	14.71	(35.30)
Comp.	14	10	.74	5.63	1.21	11.57	8.26	(19.83)
D. Span	10	7	.67	8.55	1.68	5.95	4.17	(10.12)
Arith.	13	6	.62	11.17	2.06	6.31	2.91	(9.22)
Simil.	13	7	.71	5.13	1.22	10.66	5.74	(16.40)
Performance tests								
P. Arr.	10	7	.64	9.20	1.82	5.49	3.85	(9.34)
P. Compl.	14	9	.83	5.31	.95	14.74	9.47	(24.21)
Bl. Des.	15	10	.84	7.56	1.10	13.64	9.09	(22.73)
Obj. A.	12	7	.69	5.54	1.31	9.16	5.34	(14.50)
D. Symb.	9	8	.80	5.62	1.06	8.49	7.55	(16.04)
					Sum	(106.60)	(71.09)	(177.69)

Summary of Findings

Source of Variation	SS	df	MS	R_{ck}	R_P	F	P
Total	373.49	19					
C	297.94	9					
K	63.05	1	63.05			63.05	.01
CK	12.50	9	1.39	.28	.72	1.39	—
Residual		(158)	1.00				

† The r_{tt}, sd_t, and $\sigma_{meas.}$ are obtained from data presented by Derner *et al.* (1950).

The analysis of the data in Table 8 also indicates that $R_{ck} = .28$, so that $R_P = 1 - .28 = .72$. The F of 1.39 which corresponds to R_{ck} is not significant ($P > .10$), indicating that the two profiles do not differ, hence can be considered to belong to the same pattern of subtest scores. The R_P of .72 similarly indicates a relatively high degree of congruence between these two profiles.

In evaluating any R_P it should be recalled that this measure is used because R_{ck} seems to have certain (possible) disadvantages: namely, that the numerical value of R_{ck} decreases as the profiles become more alike (see Chapter II, Special Case 2), and also that R_{ck} is distributed from 0 to $+1$. But, since $R_P = 1 - R_{ck}$, the value of R_P increases as the profiles become more alike, so that R_P also has the (possible) disadvantage of being distributed from 0 to $+1$, with the result that it may seem to be "too low" in certain cases. That is to say, R_P is not distributed as r—the scale by which many research workers judge the magnitude of a correlation coefficient or, more generally, of a measure of association, relationship, or similarity.

The significance of any R_P can be determined merely by taking the reciprocal of the table value of F at the .01 or .05 level with the df for R_{ck}. For any level of significance the value of R_P will, of course, be determined by the df in the numerator and in the denominator of F_{ck}. Table 9 is provided to familiarize the reader with a sample set of R_P's and their corresponding P-values. In this table we have listed the df for the numerator and have assumed 100 df in the denominator

TABLE 9
Illustrative Sample of R_P's Significant at the .05 and .01 Levels†

df_{n_1}	P-value .05	.01	df_{n_1}	P-value .05	.01	df_{n_1}	P-value .05	.01
1	.254	.145	7	.476	.335	14	.559	.442
2	.324	.207	8	.493	.372	16	.571	.457
3	.370	.251	9	.508	.386	20	.595	.485
4	.407	.285	10	.521	.398	24	.613	.505
5	.435	.313	11	.532	.412	30	.637	.529
6	.457	.334	12	.540	.424	40	.667	.559

† For 100 df in the denominator of F_{ck}, $R_P = 1/F_{ck}$; thus, for 1 and 100 df, $F = 3.94$; $R_{ck} = .254$.

of F_{ck}. For these df an obtained R_P indicates *a lack of discrepancy among the profile scores if it exceeds the critical value* of R_P in Table 9. By the same procedure the significance of the R_P in Table 8 (assuming 9 and 150 df) is: for $P = .05$, $R_P = 1/1.94 = .515$; for $P = .01$, $R_P = 1/2.53 = .395$. Since the R_P of .72 in Table 8 exceeds these values, we have additional evidence for assuming that, although profiles N_1 and N_2 differ in terms of level, they do not differ in terms of pattern; that is, they show a parallel pattern.

If persons drawn from the same clinical syndrome show similar profiles, which fact is reflected in a low value of R_{ck} (or high value of R_P), one would expect also that persons from syndromes which are quite different from one another would show a low R_P. To test this expectation the profiles of a case designated "organic brain disease" (O_1) and another designated "adolescent psychopath" (P_1) were analyzed. The results are given in Table 10.

TABLE 10

Analysis of Wechsler-Bellevue Scores of Cases Designated Organic Brain Disease (O_1) and Adolescent Psychopath (P_1) Using Stabilized Scores†

Verbal tests	O_1	P_1	Sum	Performance tests	O_1	P_1	Sum
Inf.	20.59	14.71	(35.30)	P. Arr.	4.95	6.59	(11.54)
Comp.	9.92	9.09	(19.01)	P. Compl.	8.42	10.53	(18.95)
D. Span	7.74	3.57	(11.31)	B. Des.	3.64	13.64	(17.28)
Arith.	4.37	2.91	(7.28)	Obj. A.	.76	12.21	(12.97)
Simil.	9.02	4.10	(13.12)	D. Symb.	2.83	11.32	(14.15)
Sum V's	(51.64)	(34.38)		Sum P's	(20.60)	(54.29)	
				Sum V's	(51.64)	(34.38)	
				Totals	(72.24)	(88.67)	

Summary of Findings

Source of Variation	SS	df	MS	R_{ck}	R_P	F	P
Total	459.97	19					
C	265.32	9					
K	13.50	1	13.50			13.50	.01
CK	181.15	9	20.13	.95	.05	20.13	.01
Residual		(158)	1.00				

† The S-scores in this table were obtained in the manner described in the text and in Table 8. The standardized scores given by Wechsler (1944, pp. 161, 164) can be obtained by multiplying the S-scores for each subtest by the corresponding $\sigma_{meas.}$ given in Table 8.

In this example we find that the S-scores of these two persons differ in terms of their over-all level (F for 1 and 158 df is 13.50) and also their pattern of scores. The latter result is indicated by several findings: the value of F_{ck} for 9 and 158 df is 20.13 and the value of R_P is only .05. Furthermore examination of the scores in Table 10 suggests that an important difference between these two profiles is not specified in these findings, namely, that O_1 seems to perform better on the verbal scales whereas P_1 seems to perform better on the performance scales taken as a whole. This interaction between the V-P and O_1-P_1 classifications may be obtained by partitioning the SS and df for the CK interaction. Specifically, we can compute the interaction sums of squares based on the sums of a 2 × 2 table as follows:

$$\frac{[(51.64 + 54.29) - (20.60 + 34.38)]^2}{20} = \frac{(50.95)^2}{20} = 129.80$$

This value is the SS and also the MS for the interaction among the four sums since 1 df is involved in this comparison. The appropriate F is 129.80/1 = 129.80 for 1 and 158 df. This F clearly indicates that O_1 and P_1 differ in their over-all response to the verbal and performance subtests.[4]

G. ILLUSTRATION OF THE METHOD WITH MMPI DATA

Certain additional aspects of the analysis of profile scores may be illustrated by data obtained from administrations of the Minnesota Multiphasic Personality Inventory.[5] This test, like a

---

[4] It will be noted that no attention has been paid to the mean squares for the subtests (C) in Tables 8 and 10, because we are interested in studying the interaction between subtests and persons, not in the effects due to the subtests themselves (see also Chapter V, Special Case 3). Also, the method of analyzing profile scores given here is not limited to $k = 2$. For example, if we analyze the profiles for the three "psychopaths" given by Wechsler, we find that the profiles differ both in level (F for 2 and 158 $df = 15.42$; $P = .01$) and pattern ($R_P = .36$; F_{ck} for 18 and 158 $df = 2.74$; $P = .01$), so that these three profiles may be said to form a mixed pattern.

[5] I am grateful to Dr. Robert E. Harris of the Langley Porter Clinic, San Francisco, California, who provided the MMPI data analyzed in this chapter. For a description of the nine MMPI scales see footnote on page 107.

variety of others, is designed so that the individual scales or subtests can be meaningfully interpreted only in relation to the total pattern of scores on all the scales. It seems, then, that MMPI data should be amenable to analysis by the pattern analytic method presented in this chapter.

In order to use this method, however, it will first be necessary to obtain a meaningful estimate of σ_e^2 from some source outside the data to be analyzed. We shall use the data reported by Rosen (1953) because he gives the values of r_{tt} and sd_t on a psychiatric population, and we shall be analyzing MMPI data from a person who presumably is a member of this population. Possible disadvantages of his data are that only 40 persons were used in the study and that the time interval between the test and retest ranged from two to seven days (four days on the average). However, the N of 40 is fairly large and, for psychiatric patients, the length of the test should reduce their memory of previous responses which would otherwise result in a sampling of nonindependent responses on the two tests.

In analyzing the W-B data we dealt with the question whether profiles from two (or more) individuals may be said to form a "pattern." We shall now analyze a set of MMPI scores to ask whether the profiles of one individual, taken on repeated occasions, are homogeneous over time. Specifically, Table 11 gives MMPI profiles of a patient who took this test five times over a period of three and a half years—once before and four times after electroshock therapy. The analysis based on all nine subtests over the five trials indicates that changes in both level and pattern occur over this time interval, since both the F of 52.01 for 4 and 40 df and the F of 9.19 for 32 and 40 df are significant at the .01 level. These changes may be due to shifts in the means and/or variances of the scores over the five trials or may arise from differential changes in the subtests over time.

The investigator may be interested in either one or both of these sources of variation, and any inter- and intrascale changes could be compared with behavioral changes and a psychological interpretation sought. They can also be studied statistically. To begin with, the trial variances were tested for homogeneity by Bartlett's test. The chi-square for 4 df is only 1.26, which is not significant (P falls between

.80 and .90), so that there is no evidence for over-all heterogeneity among the five trial variances. We have already seen that the five trial means differ ($F = 52.01$), but the significance of this F appears to be largely due to the difference between the one pre-shock and the

TABLE 11

Analysis of MMPI Scores of a Single Individual over Five Trials (One Pre-shock, Four Post-shock Trials) Using Stabilized Scores†

Scales (c)	r_{tt}	sd_t^2	$\sigma_{meas.}$	Trials (k) Before Shock 1	2	After Electric Shock 3	4	5	Sum (1-5)
Psychoneurotic scales									
Hs	.85	45.89	2.62	17.56	14.89	14.12	14.12	16.41	(77.10)
D	.80	41.83	2.89	19.72	15.22	15.22	17.65	18.34	(86.15)
Hy	.88	50.07	2.45	20.41	23.27	22.04	23.27	26.53	(115.52)
Pd	.88	30.20	1.90	38.42	22.11	21.05	23.16	26.84	(131.58)
Sum				(96.11)	(75.49)	(72.43)	(78.20)	(88.12)	
MF	.64	17.86	2.52	19.44	21.03	25.00	19.44	16.27	(101.18)
Psychotic scales									
Pa	.75	17.80	2.11	34.60	23.70	25.12	25.12	23.70	(132.24)
Pt	.80	90.44	4.25	14.82	8.00	8.00	9.18	8.71	(48.71)
Sc	.83	108.85	4.30	14.42	9.07	9.07	9.30	9.77	(51.63)
Ma	.56	23.18	3.19	22.57	14.11	11.60	12.85	14.11	(75.24)
Sum				(86.41)	(54.88)	(53.79)	(56.45)	(56.29)	
Sum for all scales				201.96	151.40	151.22	154.09	160.68	

Summary of Findings, Trials 1–5

Source of Variation	SS	df	MS	R_{ck}	R_P	F	P
Total	2073.41	44					
C (scales)	1571.18	8	196.40			21.37	.01
K (trials)	208.02	4	52.01			52.01	.01
CK	294.21	32	9.19	.89	.11	9.19	.01
Residual		(40)	1.00				

† The standardized MMPI scores are transformed to S-scores on the basis of data reported by Rosen (1953).

four post-shock trials. Although for all nine scales the difference between the four post-shock trials is statistically significant (F for 3 and 40 *df* is 2.02), the major shift in the trial means can be attributed to the electroshock therapy, which might reflect a change in the patient's general level of anxiety (or whatever the level score measures) or other behavioral changes.

We may also inquire whether the variation is consistent for the nine clinical scales. Bartlett's test, when applied to test the homogeneity of the nine subtests over the five trials, yields a chi-square of 14.68 for 8 df, which is significant at about the .07 level. Inspection of the individual scales shows that over the five trials the Hs, D, and Hy scales are much more stable, for example, than the Pd, Pt, and Ma scales. Furthermore, in addition to the size of the shifts in these scales, the direction of change should also be noted: the scores on the Hy and MF scales show a rise, whereas the other seven scales show a drop after the shock.

It is also apparent that the "psychotic" scales (Pa, Pt, Sc, Ma) as a group drop and stay low during the four post-shock trials, whereas the scores on the "psychoneurotic" scales (Hs, D, Hy, Pd) tend to rise during the post-shock trials. This difference suggests that the post-shock scores on the psychoneurotic and the psychotic scales might be analyzed separately.

A summary of findings for these analyses of the data are given in Table 12. The value of R_{ck} is estimated to be .00, so that R_P is estimated to be 1.00 in both cases. It should be noted in this connection that the *computed* mean squares for CK are .77 (psychoneurotic scales) and .72 (psychotic scales), and for the latter group of scales the MS for K is .40. It will be recalled that the $E(MS)$ for CK is made up of two components, $\sigma_e^2 + \sigma_{ck}^2$, and that the $E(MS)$ for K is made up of three components, $\sigma_e^2 + \sigma_{ck}^2 + c\sigma_k^2$. But, since $\sigma_e^2 = 1$, and we have assumed that a component of variance cannot be negative, the components σ_{ck}^2 and σ_k^2 are arbitrarily given the value of 0 on the assumption that the obtained negative values are a result of sampling errors, possibly due to the small number of df upon which the above estimates of .77, .72, and .40 are based. The estimated values in Table 12 to which this discussion applies are marked with a dagger.

(It is possible that one can approach the analysis of this type of data differently and use the CK interaction directly as the estimate of

$\sigma_e{}^2$. For one thing, the patient contributed a series of repeated scores, and this case differs from a set of k individuals who contribute one set of scores apiece. Furthermore, it can be argued that in this particular case the estimated $\sigma_e{}^2$ of 1, which is based on outside data, is in fact too large for the post-shock trials—if one of the effects of the shock is to decrease the response variability of the patient. Finally, one can argue with Nelder (1954) that the obtained estimates of components of variance should be used, even when they carry a negative sign.[6] Arguments against the use of this approach with these data are that some of the values thus obtained fall outside the range of 0 to $+1$ for R_{ck} and R_P, and that any estimates of the statistical significance of the various R's and F's would be based on only 3 and $9df$.)

The F for differences among levels is 11.54 for 3 and 40 df for the psychoneurotic scales, whereas the corresponding F for the psychotic scales is estimated to be 1.00.[7] These findings indicate that on the post-shock trials the scores on the psychoneurotic scales rose significantly, but on the psychotic scales the over-all level of these scores did not change within the limits of the estimated sampling errors.

Finally, it will be recalled that, in analyzing the profiles of two or more individuals, the effect of the scales as such was ignored so

---

[6] Nelder (1954, p. 548) states, for example, that "neither on the randomization model nor on the modified normal model is there any justification for the common practice of putting equal to zero a variance component whose estimate from an analysis is negative. The appropriate formulae should be applied as though the component were negative and no special distinction should be made." He adds, however, that "if the model used in the analysis is the orthodox normal model, then the practice of equating negative components of variance to zero is much less objectionable, and not likely to lead to much bias in the estimation of standard errors, etc."

[7] It might be meaningful in this case to compute R_L (see formula **18**) as a measure of the extent to which the level scores are homogeneous. In this example R_L for the psychoneurotic scales is .72 and it corresponds to the F of 11.54, whereas the R_L is estimated to be .00 for the psychotic scales. In some contexts R_L might be used meaningfully, for example, to describe whether the sample is homogeneous with respect to an attribute such as intelligence when one is interested in studying profile differences only.

that R's and F's were not computed on the basis of the C classification. The rationale mentioned at the time was our interest in studying the subtest-person interaction, not differences among the subtest scores themselves. In such cases, removal of the subtest effect also equates for any over-all inequalities in the subtest means, which are of no interest in connection with the problem as stated. But, when studying a series of profiles from one individual, and when the means of the subtests are presumably equal in the "population," it may be of interest to inquire whether the individual tends to obtain different scores on the various subtests. The S-scores of the patient given in

TABLE 12

Summary of Findings for the Psychoneurotic and Psychotic Scales for the Four Post-shock Trials

Source of Variation	SS	df	MS	R_{ck}	R_P	R_L	F	P
Psychoneurotic scales								
Total	290.56	15						
C (scales)	248.99	3	(83.00)				(83.00)	.01
K (trials)	34.63	3	11.54			.72	11.54	.01
CK	6.94	9	(1.00)†	(.00)†	(1.00)†			
Residual		(40)	1.00					
Psychotic scales								
Total	653.99	15						
C (scales)	646.30	3	(215.43)				(215.43)	.01
K (trials)	1.19	3	(1.00)†			(.00)	(1.00)†	
CK	6.50	9	(1.00)†	(.00)†	(1.00)†			
Residual		(40)	1.00					

† Estimates based on the $E(MS)$ where σ_e^2 is estimated from outside data.

Table 11 may be used to illustrate this point. For the five trials and nine scales, the F for differences among the scale means is 21.37 (for 8 and 32 df), which is significant at the .01 level. Furthermore, when we consider only the four psychoneurotic scales on the four post-shock trials which are summarized in Table 12, we find the F to be 83.00 (for 3 and 40 df), and the corresponding F for the psychotic scales to be 215.43 (for 3 and 40 df). Both of these F's are significant at the .01 level, and this finding bears out the obvious difference among the scores on these scales in Table 11.

H. INTRODUCTION TO THE PROBLEM OF PATTERN ANALYTIC STUDIES WITH GROUPS

We have seen that the pattern analytic method proposed in this chapter may be used to analyze *the profile scores from a set of individuals studied as a group* or *a set of profile scores from one individual*. In order to carry out such analyses, it was first necessary to be able to assume that the test units were normally and independently distributed with the same variance. The procedures discussed above were used to meet these assumptions. But *when groups of individuals contribute sets of correlated scores, the statistical problem is changed, since the individuals in the groups now become the test units*. If correlation exists within the set of scores that each individual contributes, the errors associated with the test units are not uncorrelated. Rather, the set of scores which composes the test unit can only be analyzed properly in terms of the dispersion matrix (of the variances and covariances), and the analysis is carried out on a set of vectors rather than on the set of subtest scores.[8] In other words, multivariate methods are required for the proper analysis of multivariate data (cf. Quenouille, 1950; Kendall, 1951, Ch. 28; Rao, 1952; Tatsuoka and Tiedeman, 1954; and Bock and Haggard).

Although the method discussed above is not sufficiently general to analyze rigorously the multivariate data involved in pattern analytic studies comparing groups, it can provide approximate and helpful answers to various research questions. These conditions have to do both with the nature of the tests and with the questions which the investigator wishes to ask.

If the procedure discussed in this chapter is to be used, it is necessary that the test batteries be constructed so that each subtest score is: (*i*) a normalized standardized score based on the responses of a sufficiently large referent group or "population," (*ii*) standardized on the same scale, that is, with the same means and the same standard

---

[8] It is worth noting that in the analysis of dispersion these vectors can be treated in a manner analogous to the analysis of variance based on individual scores, so that an understanding of the univariate case provides a foundation for the understanding of multivariate analysis.

deviations,[9] and (*iii*) composed of subtests which are uncorrelated. The last requirement may be met, for example, when the subtests are based on orthogonal factor analytic solutions, such as the Thurstones (1941) used in constructing tests for the "primary mental abilities."[10] Under these conditions a three-way analysis of variance model might be used to analyze the sets of scores contributed by groups of individuals. As a general rule, however, it is unsafe to assume that these conditions are met by the majority of standardized tests.

The questions asked by the investigator when dealing with profiles of groups of individuals usually include the following: (*i*) Does a set of profiles show any pattern and, if so, what type of pattern? (*ii*) What criteria or procedures may be used to establish the possible presence of two or more patterns? (*iii*) If two or more patterns exist, do they differ significantly? (*iv*) Assuming the existence of one or more patterns, and given a new profile, how can its pattern membership be determined? Although multivariate techniques are to be preferred in answering these questions, we shall consider each one briefly and indicate how the method proposed in this chapter might be used to obtain approximate, and sometimes satisfactory, answers to them.

(*i*) Does a set of profiles from different individuals show any pattern and, if so, what type of pattern? We have already considered this question in connection with the discussion of Tables 8, 10, 11,

---

[9] If one subtest were scored on a scale with a range from 1 to 5, and another on a scale from 6 to 10, the means of these two subtests would necessarily differ, and the estimate of the *BCMS* would be spuriously high. Or, if one subtest were scored on a scale of 3 to 7 and another on a scale of 1 to 10, the estimate of the *RMS* would be spuriously high. It is thus obvious that any value of *R* which is based on data with such inequalities among the scales will not be meaningful. If differences do exist among the means and/or the standard deviations of the scales, such differences should be corrected before *R* is computed. Otherwise the effects of the scalar inequalities will be confounded with any "real" differences among the profiles of scores based on them.

[10] The decision as to whether the subtests are correlated rests on whether significant covariances exist in the dispersion matrix. But the mere absence of "statistically significant" covariances cannot serve as the only criterion for assuming that the subtests are independent, since significance in this sense is determined in part by the size of the sample. The development of subtests which are constructed to be independent would avoid this difficulty.

and 12. We saw, for example, that in Table 10 individual P_1 performed better on the performance subtests whereas individual O_1 performed better on the verbal subtests of the Wechsler-Bellevue test. This interaction can be tested on groups merely by placing the scores of different individuals in each of the four cells of a 2×2 table. One could assign, say, 30 "psychopaths" selected at random who take only the verbal subtests, 30 different "psychopaths" who take only the performance subtests, 30 "organics" who take only the verbal subtests, and 30 different "organics" who take only the performance subtests. If this were done, the test units (here the score based on the five subtests taken as a unit) would not appear in more than one cell, which would be parallel to an agricultural design for which the analysis of variance technique was developed. If the interaction proved statistically significant, the finding would apply to the population of such persons and tests without reference to the performance of any one person on these tests.

Usually, however, the investigator wishes to make statements which pertain to a group of particular individuals; then a congruent or parallel pattern can be said to exist when the person-subtest interaction for a set of profiles is negligible or nonsignificant; that is, when R_{ek} is low so that R_P is high. Thus in Table 8 we find that N_1 and N_2 differ in level but not in the pattern of their profile scores, so that a parallel pattern may be said to exist. The three "psychopaths," on the other hand, show a mixed pattern—or a lack of pattern in the usual sense. In Table 11 the patient's scores also show a mixed pattern when all nine MMPI subtests over all five trials are analyzed, but when the psychoneurotic scales are taken over the four post-shock trials a parallel pattern may be said to exist, as a congruent pattern exists among the four psychotic scales over these four trials.

(*ii*) What criteria or procedures may be used to establish the possible presence of two or more patterns? Apart from multivariate methods, which enable one to assign individuals to groups on the basis of their profile scores with maximal and known precision, the investigator is forced to rely on one of several approximate methods to form groups of profiles. The results of cluster or factor analysis in which persons are intercorrelated, clinical diagnoses or various behavorial criteria or reliance on theoretical or empirical expectations of what the pattern should be like may be used to form such tentative groupings. After such groups are formed, the procedures referred to above may be used to determine the magnitude of the profile level differences and/or person-subtest interactions, and the findings expressed in terms of the appropriate R's and F's. Patterns obtained by such methods may be "refined" by the removal of one or more profiles which differ most from the remainder of the profiles in the tentative pattern, with the result that R_P will be increased.

(*iii*) If two or more patterns exist, do they differ significantly? This question, like the preceding one, can best be answered by multivariate techniques. However, when two or more independent samples are obtained and R_P is computed for each, it is possible to determine the significance levels for each R_P by the method given in connection with Table 9. If, then, the profiles from two or more patterns are combined and a single analysis performed, one can gain some idea of whether the patterns taken separately differ. Thus, if R_P for each of two patterns is significant at the .01 level but the combined R_P is significant at, say, the .40 level, the investigator has reason to believe that, practically speaking, two different patterns exist.

(*iv*) Assuming the existence of one or more patterns, and given a new profile, how can its pattern membership be determined? Regardless of the method by which a pattern is formed, it is to be expected that the profiles which make it up will, by and large, be similar in terms of their level and/or profile scores. But it is also to be expected that the individual profiles will differ to a greater or lesser degree in these respects, so that some measure of profile similarity is needed before one can say that a pattern is established. One method for determining the existence of a pattern is to perform the analysis described in this chapter, in order to determine at a specified level of significance, or a specified value of R, whether the level differences and/or person-subtest interactions can be considered small enough to be disregarded.

It is thus possible to set standards which must be met before a set of profiles can be said to form a pattern. The rigor of such standards will, of course, depend on the investigator's interests and intended use of the pattern. Specifically, if the over-all profile level is considered an important aspect of the pattern, the investigator may require that the profiles which make up the pattern must not differ in terms of a specified P-value for F_L. Or, if the level is not considered important, or if it is not clear that the test measures level meaningfully, the investigator may choose to disregard F_L in the analysis of the set of profiles. The possible magnitude of the person-subtest interaction, as indicated by F_{ck}, can be determined in the same manner. As a rule, however, we can assume that the person-subtest interaction must be negligible or nonsignificant in terms of a specified P-value (e.g., .01, .05, .10, etc.) for a pattern to be defined in terms of a set of profiles. Similarly, one can define R_P as a measure of distance and require that it reaches a specified value, such as .70 or .85, before a set of profiles is said to form a pattern.

If one or more patterns can be thus defined, we can then compute the means of each of the subtest scores of the profiles in the pattern as a working definition of that pattern, thus forming "pattern profiles."[11] It is then possible to compare any individual profiles with any pattern profiles which are based on the set of subtest means of an established pattern by the method described in this chapter. It is to be expected that the same statistical criteria that were used to define the pattern in the first place will be used to determine the pattern-membership of any individual profiles.

———————

[11] The mean of the subtest scores, or pattern profile, can also be used to obtain close approximations of factor analytic results. Specifically, when MMPI and similar types of data are used, the "factor pattern" can be obtained by correlating individual profiles with pattern profiles, and the "factor structure" can be obtained by correlating the pattern profiles (Haggard and Chapman).

VIII

the application of
intraclass correlation to data
in the form of ranks

A. INTRODUCTION

The purpose of this chapter is to introduce the use of the coefficient of intraclass correlation to data in the form of ranks for those research workers who, from choice or necessity, deal with this type of data. Although ranks have been used for over two hundred years to express preference ordering, it was not until Spearman (1904) introduced the concept of the rank order correlation coefficient as a measure of agreement between two sets of rankings that this type of data was used extensively in research work. But many psychologists, educators, and other research workers have tended to consider ranks as makeshifts or poor substitutes for variate measurements, and have used ranking methods because of computational ease or because they considered that "approximate answers" were sufficient in their work. In recent years, however, statisticians (e.g., Hotelling and Pabst, 1936; Kruskal and Wallis, 1952; Kendall, 1955; Fraser, 1957) have become interested in developing a general theory for ranks and other nonparametric statistics. As a result of their work it is becoming increasingly apparent that in many research situations ranking methods should be used in preference to the classical statistical procedures.

The process of ranking rests on the assumption that all members of the set of entities (persons, objects, events, or other phenomena) under consideration possess some identifiable attribute in varying degrees. When the members of the set are arranged only in terms of the order of magnitude of the attribute, and when ordinal numbers are assigned according to that order, the members of the set are said to be ranked. Customarily, the member which possesses the greatest amount of the attribute in question is assigned the ordinal number or rank of "1," the member which possesses the next largest amount of the attribute is assigned the rank of "2," and so on, until all the members have been assigned a number. This custom of assigning ranks is quite arbitrary, and some argue that it would be preferable to assign the rank of "1" to the member which possesses the smallest amount of the attribute in question, so that the direction of the rankings would correspond to that of the usual measurement system.

The set of ranks forms a ranking, to which the fundamental arithmetic operations of adding, subtracting, multiplying, and dividing are applied. Although ordinal numbers do not "obey" all the rules of cardinal arithmetic, the transition from ordinal to cardinal numbers (without recourse to a variate scale) may be said to rest on the fact that in assigning ranks the essential operation involves the counting and ordering of objects in terms of some attribute, which operation uses cardinal numbers (cf. Kendall, 1955, p. 1). But, in any case, ranks can be thought of and worked with as though they were cardinal numbers, no matter how they arise.

Ranks may arise in various ways and, in general, the manner by which the ranks are obtained will determine the nature of the investigator's research questions. For example, ranks may have two rather different origins: (*i*) those based on an "objective" or "true" scale (or one which is presumed to exist), and (*ii*) those obtained when no such criterion scale is available. In case (*i*), actual measurements (e.g., height) may be transformed into ranks, or the criterion scale may be based on the consensus of a group of "experts." Two or more such rankings can be compared, of course, or other sets of rankings may be compared with the criterion. When the other rankings are compared with the criterion ranking, the investigator is able to determine the extent to which the other rankings agree with the criterion. Here the investigator is asking questions pertaining to the accuracy of the other rankings, or their "validity." In case (*ii*), when no criterion scale is available, the comparison of a set of rankings provides a measure of the degree of their agreement or concordance. This question differs from the former, and pertains to what might be called inter-judge "reliability." We shall be concerned primarily with the latter type of research question.

After data in the form of ranks have been obtained, it is possible to transform the ranks into normalized scores and to apply the traditional measures of correlation and tests of significance which are appropriate for measurement data.[1] But it is questionable whether any real advantage is to be gained by transforming ranks into variate-like scores. Since only one attribute can be ranked at a time, the statistical model that may be used will be relatively simple and, furthermore, a wide variety of nonparametric techniques is now available for the analysis of data in the form of ranks (e.g., Siegel, 1956; Fraser, 1957).

Under certain conditions the use of a normalizing transformation would result in a distortion or misrepresentation of either the nature of the operations by which the ranks are obtained or of the distribution of the attribute under investigation. Since it is not possible to quantify such attributes as "frustration tolerance" or "ego strength" more precisely than in terms of their order of magnitude, it would be presumptuous to attempt to put such observations on a more refined scale. Also, there is frequently no ground for assuming that the attribute in question is normally distributed, and normalizing the ranks would not normalize the distribution of the attribute in the population. Such assumptions are not involved in the use of ranks or other nonparametric statistics. In fact, there is frequently more reason to transform quantitative scores into ranks than vice versa. This

---

[1] Tables for transforming ranks into normalized scores have been given by Fisher and Yates (1953, Table XX), and Walker and Lev (1953, Table XX).

procedure might be justified when it is unsafe to make any assumptions regarding the normality of the distribution underlying the obtained scores, or whenever such an assumption is clearly violated.

B. SOME PROPERTIES OF INTRACLASS CORRELATION WITH RANKS

The present chapter is concerned with summarizing data in the form of ranks, where k rankings of c entities form a $c \times k$ matrix,[2] whereas the previous chapters dealt with the analysis of data obtained by the measurement of attributes of persons, objects, events, or other phenomena. In considering the analysis of measurement data we saw that R is related to r (and hence to $\bar{r}$) under certain conditions. That is to say, r may be thought of as a special case of R or, conversely, R may be thought of as a generalization of r when the data are in terms of the same scale of measurement and the k means and variances are equal.

It can be shown that, when k rankings are of equal size, the means and the variances of the rankings are also equal. Let us assume that k judges have ranked c persons or objects on some trait so that we have a $c \times k$ matrix (with one rank per cell), and let us assume also that there are no tied ranks in any of the k rankings. Since the value of c is constant in a $c \times k$ matrix, and since the sum of any k rankings can be obtained by $c(c + 1)/2$, it is clear that each of the k rankings will have the same sum and hence the same mean. Furthermore, since the sum of squares of any k ranking can be obtained by $(c^3 - c)/12$, it is clear that each of the k rankings will have the same sum of squares and hence the same variance. The question then arises whether a coefficient of intraclass correlation exists for data in the form of ranks (R_r) which is similarly related to rho (ρ), Spearman's rank

---

[2] In most treatments of ranks in a $c \times k$ matrix, the number of entities ranked is given the symbol n (instead of c) and the number of judges or rankings is given the symbol m (instead of k). The notation used in this chapter was chosen to be consistent with the symbols used in the analysis of a two-way classification with measurement data.

order coefficient of correlation, and particularly whether R_r equals $\bar{\rho}$, the average of a set of k rank order correlation coefficients.

Since ρ may be thought of as the rank order form of r ("Student," 1921), one would expect R_r to be related to ρ in the limiting case where only two rankings are to be compared. But this case is of no great practical interest; since the formula for ρ is already familiar to research workers, it is easily computed and its statistical significance can be determined. Rather, if R_r is to be of more than theoretical interest, it should provide a measure of the over-all correlation (or agreement or concordance) among a set of k rankings where $k > 2$. But, since $R = \bar{r}$ when the k means and variances are equal, we expect that R_r will equal $\bar{\rho}$ and hence can be computed when $\bar{\rho}$ is desired. Indeed, Kendall (1952, p. 411) has already shown that $\bar{\rho}$ is the intraclass coefficient of correlation when the k sets of ranks are considered variate values.[3]

Since $R_r = \bar{\rho}$ under the conditions specified above, it is relevant to ask whether the various properties of R which were discussed in connection with measurement data (Chapter III) will apply also to R_r, the measure which is appropriate for data in the form of ranks. Properties 1, 2, and 3 of R hold equally well for R_r. That is to say, the limiting values of R_r are $-1/(k-1)$ and $+1$, hence as k increases the minimal value of R_r will approach 0. Furthermore R_r is related to F_r in the same manner as R is related to F, as shown by formula 6.

Property 4 of R, which has to do with its statistical significance, does not apply in all respects as a corresponding property R_r. Even though F_r is used to determine the "statistical significance" of R_r, the basis for such a statement is not the same for ranks as for measurement data. Thus in the "null case," where the significance test

---

[3] Kendall (1952, p. 436) also notes that Kelley (1923) suggested that $\bar{\rho}$ be used as a measure of concordance in rankings. Kelley's method (pp. 217–221) gives results very close to those obtained by the method presented in this chapter. Kelley also deals with certain related problems in the analysis of ranked data, such as the correlation between one judge and all the other judges in order to determine which judge agrees most closely with the average opinion of the other judges. This problem is similar to that of determining "pattern membership," as discussed in Chapter VII. Lyerly (1952) also has given a procedure for computing $\bar{\rho}$ directly from a $c \times k$ matrix and for determining its significance in the null case.

involves a statement of the probability that the obtained correlation *differs from zero*, the considerations which apply for R are not the same as those which apply in a test of the significance of R_r. With measurement data, the statistic F may be used to test the null hypothesis (in terms of a specified P-value or level of significance) that the correlation is greater than zero. If the obtained R is not compatible with such a hypothesis—that is, cannot be accounted for in terms of sampling variations—the R in question is said to be "significant" at the level specified. Or, in other words, one rejects the hypothesis that at the .01, .05, or some other level of significance the obtained R is drawn from a population with the parameter $\tilde{R} = 0$.

When data are in the form of ranks, reference to "population parameters" which are independent of sample size, etc. cannot be made, since population parameters in this sense do not exist for ranks. Rather, tests of significance involving ranks rest on the fact that, for any ranking of a given size c, it is possible to determine all the permutations of the numbers 1, . . ., c. From this information it is then possible to determine the probability that obtained rankings of size c could have arisen by being chosen at random from all possible permutations of rankings of size c. Furthermore, when a set of rankings is involved, it is necessary that each of the rankings be independent in the sense that, in a $c \times k$ matrix, the ck interaction should be zero. If the k rankings are independent in this sense, the variation among the ranks within classes may be used as the proper error term in computing F_r in the one-way analysis of variance. (In this connection it should be noted that when c and k are small certain continuity corrections are needed to compute R_r and F_r; the necessary adjustments will be considered in section E of this chapter.)

Although a parallel thus exists in the null case for measurements and ranks, with the result that the statistical significance of both R and R_r can be determined, no such parallel exists at present for the non-null case (cf. Property 5 of R). That is to say, one can estimate the confidence limits of R but not of R_r. The reason for this is that the distributions of ranks for the non-null case (or nonrandom distributions of ranks) is not known. However, in view of the fact that, as c and k increase in size, the distributions of permutations of ranks approximate the F distribution in the null case (so that when c and k are sufficiently large ranks may be treated essentially as variate measures), and the fact that the F distribution may be used also for the non-null case, it seems reasonable to expect that for large values of c and k approximate confidence limits may be obtained for R_r as well as for R.

With reference to Properties 6 and 7 of R, we have already seen that $R_r = \bar{\rho}$, the average of k rank order correlation coefficients. From this relation it follows that, when c entities are ranked by k judges, only the differences among the c means can be analyzed since the means and the variances of the k's are, by definition, equal. It is true, of course, that one can sometimes re-rank the data in a $c \times k$ matrix along the other dimension, but in this case the k means may vary but the c means will be equal. Consequently, since only one attribute can be ranked at a time, the analysis is limited to a one-way classification design.

But, even though any particular analysis of ranks is limited to a one-way design, it should be noted that the investigator has a good deal of latitude in defining the C and K classifications. He can, for example, have one judge rank k persons on c traits, or have k judges rank c persons on one trait, or have one judge rank c persons on one trait on k occasions, and so on. If the k rankings are independent, R_r will give an over-all measure of the agreement, concordance, or correlation among the k sets of rankings, and F_r can be used to determine the statistical significance of this measure.

C. THE COMPUTATION OF R_r

The method of computing R_r is analogous to the method of computing R from a one-way classification. Thus, given a $c \times k$ matrix of ranks with one rank per cell and assuming that tied ranks do not exist, let us assume that c entities are ranked by k judges. As we have seen, the k sums will be equal in this case and, if there is any agreement, concordance, or correlation among the rankings, the c sums will vary. Since R is the analogue of R_r, it will be apparent that we shall need to compute only the total sum of squares for the matrix and the between-classes sum of squares, and that the within-classes sum of squares can be obtained by subtracting the latter from the former. The necessary sums of squares may be obtained as follows:

Total sum of squares for ranks with $(ck - 1)$ *df*:

21]
$$TSS_r = \frac{k(c^3 - c)}{12}$$

Between-classes sum of squares for ranks with $(c - 1)$ *df*:

22]
$$BCSS_r = \frac{\sum X_c^2}{k} - \frac{ck(c + 1)^2}{4}$$

where X_c is the sum of ranks in class c.

Within-classes sum of squares for ranks with $(c - 1)(k - 1)$ *df*:

23]
$$WSS_r = TSS_r - BCSS_r$$

The between-classes mean square $(BCMS_r)$ and within-classes mean square (WMS_r) for ranks are obtained by dividing the $BCSS_r$ and WSS_r by their respective *df*. And, as with F and R for measurement data, F_r and R_r can then be defined as follows:

24]
$$F_r = \frac{BCMS_r}{WMS_r}$$

and

25]
$$R_r = \frac{BCMS_r - WMS_r}{BCMS_r + (k - 1)WMS_r} = \frac{F_r - 1}{F_r + (k - 1)}$$

The computation of R_r can now be illustrated by converting the data in Table 6 into ranks. In accordance with convention, the largest score in each k distribution is given the rank "1," and so on; and, when two or more of the scores are the same, the median or mid-rank method is used to assign the same rank to each of the tied scores. The data transformed into ranks are given in Table 13.

We are now able to compare the R of .46 obtained from the data in Table 6 with the R_r of .40 (not corrected for ties) obtained from the ranks in Table 13. The difference between these two coefficients of intraclass correlation is presumably due to the "loss of information" incurred in the transformation of measurement data into ranks. This transformation usually results in a lowering of the correlation coefficient, but the difference between such analogous coefficients is often rather small.

It was mentioned earlier that, when data are transformed into ranks, it is sometimes meaningful to rank the scores in a $c \times k$ matrix twice—once according to each of the classifications. The data in Table 3 may be used to illustrate this possibility, particularly since R's were estimated in terms of both the C and the K classifications. The results of this double ranking are given in Table 14, and we find

TABLE 13
Data in Table 6 Transformed into Ranks

Topic	1	2	3	4	5	Sum X_c
			Author			
1	19	16	24	19	11	89
2	18	22½	17	9	17½	84
3	10½	18	4	21½	3½	57½
4	10½	22½	10½	5	8	56½
5	17	22½	15	4	20	78½
6	2	3	5	16	3½	29½
7	16	14	9	12½	19	70½
8	4	13	8	3	7	35
9	15	7½	7	10	14½	54
10	5	1	14	2	2	24
11	1	2	1	1	6	11
12	12	17	22	18	14½	83½
13	8	9	12	14	17½	60½
14	6	11½	2	8	10	37½
15	9	11½	17	6	13	56½
16	24	22½	24	24	12	106½
17	23	22½	24	24	23	116½
18	25	22½	20	20	1	88½
19	20½	6	17	7	21	71½
20	22	10	6	15	22	75
21	20½	19	10½	21½	9	80½
22	13	4	21	12½	16	66½
23	14	7½	13	17	24	75½
24	3	5	3	11	5	27
25	7	15	19	24	25	90
Sum X_k	325	325	325	325	325	1625
Correction for ties	1.0	+18.5	+4.5	+3.0	+1.5	$= \Sigma C_t = 28.5$

Computations

Total SS (124 df) $= \dfrac{5(15{,}625 - 25)}{12} = 6500.0$

Between-classes SS (24 df) $= 89.0^2 + 84.0^2 + 57.5^2 + \ldots$

$$+ \frac{90.0^2}{5} - \frac{ck(c + 1)^2}{4}$$

$$= 24{,}492.6 - \frac{125(26^2)}{4}$$

$$= 24{,}492.6 - 21{,}125 = 3367.6$$

Within SS (96 df) $=   6500.0 - 3367.6 = 3132.4$

Summary of Findings†

Source of Variation	SS	df	MS	F_r	R_r	(R)‡	$W = \eta_r^2$
Total	6500.0	124					
C	3367.6	24	140.32	4.30	.40	(.46)	(.52)
K	0.0	4					
CK	3132.4	96	32.63				

† Values not corrected for tied ranks.

‡ R given in Table 6 for these data in the form of measurements.

that, when the subjects are ranked, R_r is .66, as compared with the R of .77 obtained from the original data. However, when the trials are ranked, $R_r = .38$, which is slightly higher than the corresponding R of .37. This result, which occasionally occurs, may be understood by comparing the relative variation of the trial scores with that of the within-subject variation over trials (see Table 3). In the discussion of these data in Chapter IV, it was noted that the subjects-trials inter-action is confounded with the within-subject variation, so that the R of .37 is underestimated to some degree. But, when the trial scores are transformed into ranks, the "interaction" information is removed, since the trial sums and variances are equalized. The R_r of .38, then, is not subject to the effect of inflating the within-subject variation as is the R of .37 given in Table 3.

A double ranking of the scores in a $c \times k$ matrix can be done by one of two procedures: by leaving the C and K classifications as they are and interchanging the c's and k's in formulas **21** to **25**, or by interchanging the C and K classifications and leaving unchanged the

c's and k's in these formulas. The latter procedure is generally preferable because it is less confusing in practice; it was used in connection with Table 14.

The $c \times k$ analysis of variance matrix for ranks can be used to estimate relationships somewhat more complex than those we have considered thus far. Schultz (1945), for example, cites data which was used to estimate relationships among socio-economic status, the level of college aptitude, and the degree of college attendance for men and women separately. He used six levels of socio-economic status and eight levels of college aptitude, as measured by a psychological examination, and entered the per cent of college attendance in each

TABLE 14
Summary of Findings when Data in Table 3 are Transformed into Ranks†

Source of Variation	SS	df	MS	F_r	R_r	(R)‡	$(W = \eta_r{}^2)$§
Subjects ranked ($c = 4$; $k = 5$)							
Total	25.0	19					
Subjects	18.3	3	6.10	10.89	.66	(.77)	(.73)
Trials	0.0	4					
Within	6.7	12	.56				
Trials ranked ($c = 5$; $k = 4$)							
Total	40.0	19					
Subjects	0.0	3					
Trials	21.5	4	5.38	3.49	.38	(.37)	(.54)
Within	18.5	12	1.54				

† The values in this table are not corrected for the effect of tied ranks. For corrected values see section D of this chapter.
‡ R's given in Table 3 for these data in the form of measurements.
§ $W = \eta_r{}^2$: Statistics proposed by Kendall and Smith (1939) and Wallis (1939) respectively. See also section F of text.

of the cells in this $c \times k$ matrix. The percentage data were then transformed into ranks. When his data for males are ranked in terms of the students' socio-economic status, it is found that $R_r = .50$ with a corresponding F_r of 8.89 for 5 and 35 df. Similarly, when these data are ranked in terms of the students' level of college aptitude, it is found that $R_r = .68$ with a corresponding F_r of 13.96 for 7 and 35 df. The data for the women in his study could be analyzed by the same procedure and the R_r's compared. It is thus possible to extend the analysis of ranked data to more elaborate experimental designs if the data were originally in measurement form. If the original data are in the form of ranks, however, only the one-way analysis can be made because only one attribute can be ranked at a time.

Finally, we can also compute R_r as an estimate of the reliability of the mean of k sets of rankings. We saw in Chapter VI that R, as an estimate of reliability, may be expressed in several forms, one of which pertains to the consistency of the units within a test. An analogous expression for data in the form of ranks may be obtained by adjusting R_r by the Spearman-Brown formula as follows:

$$26] \qquad R_r{}^* = \frac{kR_r}{1 + (k - 1)R_r}$$

in which case $R_r{}^*$ is analogous to the Kuder-Richardson formula for ranked data (cf. Horst, 1949). And, as with R, the same result can also be obtained from the corresponding F for ranked data:

$$27] \qquad R_r{}^* = 1 - \frac{1}{F_r}$$

In this section we have considered only the analysis of a $c \times k$ matrix with one rank or observation per cell. Recently Durbin (1951) has given a method for analyzing k rankings of equal size in which some of the observations are missing, and Benard and van Elteren (1953) have given a generalization applicable to cases where the number of observations per cell may be either zero or any positive integer.[4]

D. THE PROBLEM OF TIED RANKS

In order to assign ranks, a judge must be able to distinguish differences in the degree to which the particular attribute under con-

---

[4] For other discussions of the analysis of ranks in a $c \times k$ matrix see, for example, Kelley, 1923; Friedman, 1937, 1940; Wallis, 1939; Kendall and Smith, 1939; Durbin, 1951; Ehrenberg, 1952; Kruskal and Wallis, 1952; Lyerly, 1952; Benard and van Elteren, 1953; Walker and Lev, 1953; Edwards, 1954*a*; Jonckheere, 1954*a*, *b*; Kendall, 1955; Siegel, 1956; and Fraser, 1957.

sideration is present in the persons or objects being ranked. If such distinctions cannot be made, he is forced to rely on some other method of assigning the ranks, since the number of ranks must equal the number of persons or objects being ranked. The usual procedure is to give the same rank to all the members of the set which cannot be thus distinguished. Tied ranks also arise when the judge might have made the necessary distinctions but was not required to do so at the time, as would be the case if he initially used a five-point scale to rate ten persons on some trait. If such data were later transformed into ranks, ties would occur since two or more of the persons would receive the same rating, and hence the same rank. Ties among ranks also occur when measurement data are transformed into rankings and two or more of the initial scores are the same, as are the data given, for example, in Tables 3 and 6.

The effect of tied ranks is to decrease the variance of the ranking in which the ties occur. (If all ranks are tied, the variance is zero.) If ties occur and the usual median or mid-rank method of dealing with tied ranks is used, the k means will remain equal but the k variances will differ, depending on the number of ties in the ranking. But we have seen that the k means and variances are assumed to be equal in the one-way analysis of a $c \times k$ matrix of ranks, so that is it necessary to make some adjustment for the existence of ties in order to equate the k variances. Several methods have been proposed.

The appropriate method of adjusting for the existence of tied ranks will depend in part on the investigator's research problem and purposes. Let us consider first the general case of estimating the degree of concordance or agreement among a set of k rankings. Two methods have been proposed for dealing with this case. One method is to assign the ranks at random within the set of tied ranks. Kruskal and Wallis (1952) have discussed this method and observed that, although it has certain theoretical advantages, in practice the results tend not to differ appreciably from the mid-rank method.

The mid-rank method is the one most commonly used but, as we have seen, when ties occur in a ranking the variance of that ranking is decreased. "Student" (1921) showed, however, that it is possible to make the necessary correction (C_t) in the variance of any ranking when the mid-rank method is used. This correction is $C_t = (t^3 - t)/12$, where t is the number of members in the ranking with the same (tied) rank. Frequently two or more sets of tied ranks will occur in a given ranking. The correction C_t is additive for all the sets of ties in all the rankings in a $c \times k$ matrix, and the sum of all the individual corrections $(\sum C_t)$ is conveniently subtracted from the WSS_r as the proper correction before R_r and F_r are computed. (Or $\sum C_t$ could be subtracted from TSS_r, which is computed on the assumption of no tied ranks and hence is inflated to the extent of $\sum C_t$ when ties occur. When R_r and F_r are computed, it does not matter whether the correction is subtracted from TSS_r or WSS_r, but in computing W or η_r^2 it is necessary to subtract $\sum C_t$ from TSS_r.)

TABLE 15
Individual Corrections for Tied Ranks
$$[C_t = (t^3 - t)/12]\dagger$$

t	C_t	t	C_t	t	C_t	t	C_t
2	.5	8	42.0	14	227.5	20	665.0
3	2.0	9	60.0	15	280.0	21	770.0
4	5.0	10	82.5	16	340.0	22	885.5
5	10.0	11	110.0	17	408.0	23	1012.0
6	17.5	12	143.0	18	484.5	24	1150.0
7	28.0	13	182.0	19	570.0	25	1300.0

† t = number of tied ranks in a set and C_t = the correction term used to adjust WSS_r. (Note: The values in Table 15 can be used to obtain TSS_r.)

This method may be illustrated by the data in Table 13, for which $\sum C_t = 28.5$. This value is subtracted from the computed WSS_r (3132.4), and the corrected value (3103.9) is used to estimate R_r and F_r. Although 26 of the 125 ranks in Table 13 are ties, most of the t's are small so that the C_t's also are small. As a consequence, the uncorrected F_r of 4.30 is raised to only 4.34, and R_r remains unchanged at .40. Similarly, in Table 14, when the subjects are ranked, the $\sum C_t = 1.0$ and with this correction R_r is raised from .66 to .70 and, when the trials are ranked, $\sum C_t = 2.0$ and R_r is raised from .38 to .42.

It is thus apparent that unless the number of ties is considerable in relation to the size of c and k and the t's are relatively large, the effect of the correction for tied ranks tends to be of negligible importance from a practical point of view. When, however, the size of t increases, the importance of making this correction increases progressively. This fact is apparent in the increase in the size of C_t as t increases, as is shown in Table 15.

We have thus far considered only the correction for tied ranks when the question of agreement among a set of k rankings is involved. It should be noted that this method may not be appropriate when the research problem involves a comparison of rankings with some objective or quantitative scale. In this connection Kendall (1945) has suggested that the above method of correcting for tied ranks should not be used, but rather that Woodbury's (1940) method seems to be more appropriate for this case (see also Kendall, 1955, Ch. 3; and Benard and van Elteren, 1953).

E. THE STATISTICAL SIGNIFICANCE OF R_r

For large values of c and k the statistical significance of an obtained R_r can be computed from its corresponding F_r in the same manner as the P-value of R can be estimated from its corresponding F (see Property 4 of R, Chapter III). As we have seen in formula **24**, F_r is defined as $BCMS_r/WMS_r$, and the F table is entered with the df corresponding to the $BCMS_r$ and WMS_r when c and k are sufficiently large. The reason is that the probability distribution of permutations of ranks is asymptotic to, or approximates, the F distribution as c and k increase. Consequently for large values of c and k the statistical significance of any F_r (and hence R_r) can be determined from the table of the F distribution (see Table 19, Appendix I).

When the values of c and k are small, however, it is necessary to make corrections for continuity in computing F_r and R_r (see Kendall and Smith, 1939, or Friedman, 1940). The necessary adjustments have been incorporated in Tables 16 and 17, so that the significance of F_r computed from formula **24**, or R_r computed from formula **25**,

TABLE 16

Values of F_r at the .05 and .01 Levels of Significance for Small Values of c Ranks and k Rankings†

$P = .05$		c Ranks (Objects)					
		3	4	5	6	7	Additional
	3	...	...	5.02	3.88	3.32	Values for
	4	...	4.87	3.70	3.14	2.81	$c = 3$
	5	...	4.01	3.27	2.86	2.61	k F_r
k rankings	6	...	3.62	3.04	2.71	2.49	9 4.00
(judges)	8	4.22	3.26	2.82	2.55	2.37	12 3.67
	10	3.84	3.08	2.71	2.47	2.30	14 3.55
	15	3.48	2.89	2.57	2.38	2.23	16 3.45
	20	3.35	2.81	2.53	2.32	2.19	18 3.38

$P = .01$		c Ranks (Objects)					
		3	4	5	6	7	
	3	...	...	10.50	7.09	5.29	
	4	...	9.90	6.46	5.10	4.34	
	5	...	7.24	5.33	4.40	3.86	
k rankings	6	...	6.17	4.79	4.06	3.61	9 7.05
(judges)	8	7.65	5.27	4.28	3.71	3.35	12 6.17
	10	6.67	4.85	4.02	3.55	3.21	14 5.87
	15	5.74	4.43	3.75	3.34	3.06	16 5.64
	20	5.39	4.23	3.62	3.25	2.98	18 5.50

† Adapted from Friedman's (1940) Table III, which is based on Kendall and Smith's (1939) z-test with corrections for continuity, by permission of the author and editor of *Ann. math. Statist.* For larger values of c and k the critical levels of F_r can be determined directly from the F-tables.

can be determined directly. Consequently Tables 16 and 17 should be used when $c \leqslant 20$ and $k \leqslant 7$.[5]

It is now possible to compare the P-values of the coefficients of intraclass correlation computed on measurement data and recomputed after these data are transformed into ranks. For the data in Tables 6 and 13 it is clear that the R of .46 and the R_r of .40 are

---

[5] The values of F_r and R_r computed from formulas **24** and **25** differ slightly from the better estimates which can be obtained by correcting $BCMS_r$ and WMS_r for continuity. For descriptive purposes, however, the difference is too slight to be of importance, and for determining levels of significance the continuity correction of Kendall and Smith can be avoided by incorporating it into the values given in the tables of F_r and R_r. This was done in constructing Tables 16 and 17. For values of c and k smaller than those given in Tables 16 and 17, approximate values of F_r and R_r can be obtained by computing Kendall's (1955) S statistic, and either converting S to $\bar{p} = R_r$ (Kendall, 1952, p. 411), or to W, and W to F_r or R_r (see Table 18).

TABLE 17

Values of R_r at the .05 and .01 Levels of Significance for Small Values of c Ranks and k Rankings†

			c Ranks (Objects)				
$P = .05$		3	4	5	6	7	Additional
	3	...	...	.573	.490	.436	Values for
	4	...	.492	.403	.349	.312	$c = 3$
	5	...	.376	.312	.271	.243	k R_r
k rankings	6	...	.304	.254	.222	.199	9 .250
(judges)	8	.287	.220	.185	.162	.146	12 .182
	10	.222	.172	.146	.128	.115	14 .154
	15	.142	.112	.095	.084	.076	16 .133
	20	.105	.083	.071	.062	.056	18 .117
			c Ranks (Objects)				
$P = .01$		3	4	5	6	7	
	3	...	...	.760	.670	.605	
	4	...	.690	.577	.506	.455	
	5	...	.555	.464	.405	.364	
k rankings	6	...	.463	.387	.338	.303	9 .402
(judges)	8	.454	.348	.291	.253	.227	12 .301
	10	.362	.278	.232	.203	.181	14 .258
	15	.240	.186	.155	.135	.121	16 .225
	20	.180	.139	.116	.101	.090	18 .200

† Adapted from Friedman's (1940) Table III, which is based on Kendall and Smith's (1939) z-test with corrections for continuity, by permission of the author and editor of *Ann. math. Statist.* For larger values of c and k the significance of R_r can be determined directly from the F-tables.

significant at the .01 level. For the data in Tables 3 and 14 it is possible to determine the significance of the R_r's by reference to Table 17. Thus we find that the R of .77 and the corresponding R_r (corrected for tied ranks) of .70 are significant at the .01 level, as seen by the fact that in Table 17 the critical value of R_r at the .01 level for $c = 4$ and $k = 5$ is .555. Similarly the R of .37 and the corresponding R_r (corrected for tied ranks) of .42 are significant at the .05 level, as seen by the fact that the critical value of R_r at the .05 level for $c = 5$ and $k = 4$ is .403.

F. THE RELATION OF R_r AND F_r TO OTHER METHODS FOR ANALYZING RANKS IN A $c \times k$ MATRIX

In conclusion, it may be of interest to examine briefly how R_r and F_r are related to certain other nonparametric statistics which have been used to analyze ranks in a $c \times k$ matrix. We have already seen that $R_r = \bar{p}$, the average of k rank order correlation coefficients. The other statistical techniques that we shall consider here are: Kendall and Smith's Coefficient of Concordance (1939), W; Wallis' Correlation Ratio for Ranks (1939), η_r^2; and Friedman's Chi-Square for Ranks (1937, 1940), χ_r^2. These statistics fall into two general classes: those designed to provide a measure of agreement or relationship and those designed to serve as test-statistics, in the same sense that R and F serve these same purposes (see Chapter I).

Except for $\bar{p}$, the statistics which may be compared with R_r are W and η_r^2, since they provide a general measure of the concordance,

TABLE 18
Interrelations among R_r, $\bar{p}$, W, η_r^2, χ_r^2, and F_r

	$R_r = \bar{p}$	$W = \eta_r^2$	χ_r^2	F_r
$R_r = \bar{p}$	$\ldots$	$\dfrac{kW-1}{k-1}$	$\dfrac{1}{k-1}\left[\dfrac{\chi_r^2}{c-1}-1\right]$	$\dfrac{F_r-1}{F_r+k-1}$
$W = \eta_r^2$	$\dfrac{1+(k-1)R_r}{k}$	$\ldots$	$\dfrac{\chi_r^2}{k(c-1)}$	$\dfrac{F_r}{F_r+k-1}$
χ_r^2	$(c+1)$ $[1+(k-1)R_r]$	$k(c-1)W$	$\ldots$	$\dfrac{k(c-1)F_r}{F_r+k-1}$
F_r	$\dfrac{1+(k-1)R_r}{1-R_r}$	$\dfrac{(k-1)W}{1-W}$	$\dfrac{(k-1)\chi_r^2}{k(c-1)-\chi_r^2}$	$\ldots$

agreement, or correlation among a set of k rankings. Actually, this comparison is simplified by the fact that $W = \eta_r^2$ since the same statistic was proposed by Kendall and Smith and by Wallis independently in the same year. One difference between $W = \eta_r^2$ and R_r is that the former measure can be computed as a ratio of two sums of squares in the analysis of variance table, whereas the latter measure is computed from the mean squares and also has its analogue in R with measurement data. Also, since $W = \eta_r^2$ can be defined as the ratio $BCSS_r/TSS_r$ (see formulas **21** and **22**), its limiting values are 0 and $+1$; the limiting values of R_r, on the other hand, are $-1/(k-1)$ and $+1$. Consequently, except in the case of perfect agreement among a set of rankings (where both values will be $+1$) or in the case of complete lack of agreement with $k = \infty$ (where both values will be 0), the measure $W = \eta_r{}^2$ will always be somewhat higher than R_r computed on the same data.

These statistics may be compared in Table 13 where $W = \eta_r{}^2$ (not corrected for tied ranks) is computed as follows: $3367.6/6500.0 = .52$, which is comparable to the R_r of $.40$. If the correction for ties is made, the C_t of 28.5 is subtracted from TSS_r, so that $W = \eta_r{}^2 = 3367.6/6477.5 = .52$, which, like R_r, is unchanged by this correction for tied ranks. Similar comparisons can be made in Table 14, where we find that the $W = \eta_r{}^2$ of $.73$ is raised to $.76$, and the value for the alternate comparison of $.54$ is raised to $.57$. The statistical significance of $W = \eta_r{}^2$ and R_r, when computed from the same data, will, of course, be identical.

As test-statistics, F_r and $\chi_r{}^2$ are similar in that they provide a test of the hypothesis that the obtained arrangement of ranks in the k rankings does not deviate from a random arrangement, as evidenced by the fact that the c sums do not differ. If there is a sufficiently high degree of agreement among the rankings, the c sums will differ, and F_r and $\chi_r{}^2$ enable the investigator to reject the null hypothesis of a random arrangement of rankings at a given level of significance. Thus, in the limiting case where all the k rankings of size c agree perfectly, so that the c sums differ maximally and $R_r = +1$, it would be very unlikely indeed that such a set of rankings would have been drawn at random from the collection of all permutations of the ranks $1, \ldots, c$ for all the k rankings. The statistical significance of F_r and $\chi_r{}^2$ will be the same when these two statistics are computed on the same data.

The algebraic relationships among the nonparametric statistics which we have considered in this section are given in Table 18.

APPENDIX I

---

table 19

5 Per Cent (Roman Type) and 1 Per Cent (Bold Face Type) Points for the Distribution of F*

Reprinted, with the permission of the author and publishers, from: Snedecor (1956), Table 10.7, pp. 246–249.

* The function, $F = e$ with exponent $2z$, is computed in part from Fisher's table VI (7). Additional entries are by interpolation, mostly graphical.

n_1 degrees of freedom (for greater mean square)

Each cell gives the 5% point (upper) and 1% point (lower).

n_2	1	2	3	4	5	6	7	8	9	10	11	12	14	16	20	24	30	40	50	75	100	200	500	∞
1	161 / 4,052	200 / 4,999	216 / 5,403	225 / 5,625	230 / 5,764	234 / 5,859	237 / 5,928	239 / 5,981	241 / 6,022	242 / 6,056	243 / 6,082	244 / 6,106	245 / 6,142	246 / 6,169	248 / 6,208	249 / 6,234	250 / 6,258	251 / 6,286	252 / 6,302	253 / 6,323	253 / 6,334	254 / 6,352	254 / 6,361	254 / 6,366
2	18.51 / 98.49	19.00 / 99.00	19.16 / 99.17	19.25 / 99.25	19.30 / 99.30	19.33 / 99.33	19.36 / 99.34	19.37 / 99.36	19.38 / 99.38	19.39 / 99.40	19.40 / 99.41	19.41 / 99.42	19.42 / 99.43	19.43 / 99.44	19.44 / 99.45	19.45 / 99.46	19.46 / 99.47	19.47 / 99.48	19.47 / 99.48	19.48 / 99.49	19.49 / 99.49	19.49 / 99.49	19.50 / 99.50	19.50 / 99.50
3	10.13 / 34.12	9.55 / 30.82	9.28 / 29.46	9.12 / 28.71	9.01 / 28.24	8.94 / 27.91	8.88 / 27.67	8.84 / 27.49	8.81 / 27.34	8.78 / 27.23	8.76 / 27.13	8.74 / 27.05	8.71 / 26.92	8.69 / 26.83	8.66 / 26.69	8.64 / 26.60	8.62 / 26.50	8.60 / 26.41	8.58 / 26.35	8.57 / 26.27	8.56 / 26.23	8.54 / 26.18	8.54 / 26.14	8.53 / 26.12
4	7.71 / 21.20	6.94 / 18.00	6.59 / 16.69	6.39 / 15.98	6.26 / 15.52	6.16 / 15.21	6.09 / 14.98	6.04 / 14.80	6.00 / 14.66	5.96 / 14.54	5.93 / 14.45	5.91 / 14.37	5.87 / 14.24	5.84 / 14.15	5.80 / 14.02	5.77 / 13.93	5.74 / 13.83	5.71 / 13.74	5.70 / 13.69	5.68 / 13.61	5.66 / 13.57	5.65 / 13.52	5.64 / 13.48	5.63 / 13.46
5	6.61 / 16.26	5.79 / 13.27	5.41 / 12.06	5.19 / 11.39	5.05 / 10.97	4.95 / 10.67	4.88 / 10.45	4.82 / 10.27	4.78 / 10.15	4.74 / 10.05	4.70 / 9.96	4.68 / 9.89	4.64 / 9.77	4.60 / 9.68	4.56 / 9.55	4.53 / 9.47	4.50 / 9.38	4.46 / 9.29	4.44 / 9.24	4.42 / 9.17	4.40 / 9.13	4.38 / 9.07	4.37 / 9.04	4.36 / 9.02
6	5.99 / 13.74	5.14 / 10.92	4.76 / 9.78	4.53 / 9.15	4.39 / 8.75	4.28 / 8.47	4.21 / 8.26	4.15 / 8.10	4.10 / 7.98	4.06 / 7.87	4.03 / 7.79	4.00 / 7.72	3.96 / 7.60	3.92 / 7.52	3.87 / 7.39	3.84 / 7.31	3.81 / 7.23	3.77 / 7.14	3.75 / 7.09	3.72 / 7.02	3.71 / 6.99	3.69 / 6.94	3.68 / 6.90	3.67 / 6.88
7	5.59 / 12.25	4.74 / 9.55	4.35 / 8.45	4.12 / 7.85	3.97 / 7.46	3.87 / 7.19	3.79 / 7.00	3.73 / 6.84	3.68 / 6.71	3.63 / 6.62	3.60 / 6.54	3.57 / 6.47	3.52 / 6.35	3.49 / 6.27	3.44 / 6.15	3.41 / 6.07	3.38 / 5.98	3.34 / 5.90	3.32 / 5.85	3.29 / 5.78	3.28 / 5.75	3.25 / 5.70	3.24 / 5.67	3.23 / 5.65
8	5.32 / 11.26	4.46 / 8.65	4.07 / 7.59	3.84 / 7.01	3.69 / 6.63	3.58 / 6.37	3.50 / 6.19	3.44 / 6.03	3.39 / 5.91	3.34 / 5.82	3.31 / 5.74	3.28 / 5.67	3.23 / 5.56	3.20 / 5.48	3.15 / 5.36	3.12 / 5.28	3.08 / 5.20	3.05 / 5.11	3.03 / 5.06	3.00 / 5.00	2.98 / 4.96	2.96 / 4.91	2.94 / 4.88	2.93 / 4.86
9	5.12 / 10.56	4.26 / 8.02	3.86 / 6.99	3.63 / 6.42	3.48 / 6.06	3.37 / 5.80	3.29 / 5.62	3.23 / 5.47	3.18 / 5.35	3.13 / 5.26	3.10 / 5.18	3.07 / 5.11	3.02 / 5.00	2.98 / 4.92	2.93 / 4.80	2.90 / 4.73	2.86 / 4.64	2.82 / 4.56	2.80 / 4.51	2.77 / 4.45	2.76 / 4.41	2.73 / 4.36	2.72 / 4.33	2.71 / 4.31
10	4.96 / 10.04	4.10 / 7.56	3.71 / 6.55	3.48 / 5.99	3.33 / 5.64	3.22 / 5.39	3.14 / 5.21	3.07 / 5.06	3.02 / 4.95	2.97 / 4.85	2.94 / 4.78	2.91 / 4.71	2.86 / 4.60	2.82 / 4.52	2.77 / 4.41	2.74 / 4.33	2.70 / 4.25	2.67 / 4.17	2.64 / 4.12	2.61 / 4.05	2.59 / 4.01	2.56 / 3.96	2.55 / 3.93	2.54 / 3.91
11	4.84 / 9.65	3.98 / 7.20	3.59 / 6.22	3.36 / 5.67	3.20 / 5.32	3.09 / 5.07	3.01 / 4.88	2.95 / 4.74	2.90 / 4.63	2.86 / 4.54	2.82 / 4.46	2.79 / 4.40	2.74 / 4.29	2.70 / 4.21	2.65 / 4.10	2.61 / 4.02	2.57 / 3.94	2.53 / 3.86	2.50 / 3.80	2.47 / 3.74	2.45 / 3.70	2.42 / 3.66	2.41 / 3.62	2.40 / 3.60
12	4.75 / 9.33	3.88 / 6.93	3.49 / 5.95	3.26 / 5.41	3.11 / 5.06	3.00 / 4.82	2.92 / 4.65	2.85 / 4.50	2.80 / 4.39	2.76 / 4.30	2.72 / 4.22	2.69 / 4.16	2.64 / 4.05	2.60 / 3.98	2.54 / 3.86	2.50 / 3.78	2.46 / 3.70	2.42 / 3.61	2.40 / 3.56	2.36 / 3.49	2.35 / 3.46	2.32 / 3.41	2.31 / 3.38	2.30 / 3.36
13	4.67 / 9.07	3.80 / 6.70	3.41 / 5.74	3.18 / 5.20	3.02 / 4.86	2.92 / 4.62	2.84 / 4.44	2.77 / 4.30	2.72 / 4.19	2.67 / 4.10	2.63 / 4.02	2.60 / 3.96	2.55 / 3.85	2.51 / 3.78	2.46 / 3.67	2.42 / 3.59	2.38 / 3.51	2.34 / 3.42	2.32 / 3.37	2.28 / 3.30	2.26 / 3.27	2.24 / 3.21	2.22 / 3.18	2.21 / 3.16

n_1 degrees of freedom (for greater mean square)

n_2	1	2	3	4	5	6	7	8	9	10	11	12	14	16	20	24	30	40	50	75	100	200	500	∞	n_2
14	4.60/8.86	3.74/6.51	3.34/5.56	3.11/5.03	2.96/4.69	2.85/4.46	2.77/4.28	2.70/4.14	2.65/4.03	2.60/3.94	2.56/3.86	2.53/3.80	2.48/3.70	2.44/3.62	2.39/3.51	2.35/3.43	2.31/3.34	2.27/3.26	2.24/3.21	2.21/3.14	2.19/3.11	2.16/3.06	2.14/3.02	2.13/3.00	14
15	4.54/8.68	3.68/6.36	3.29/5.42	3.06/4.89	2.90/4.56	2.79/4.32	2.70/4.14	2.64/4.00	2.59/3.89	2.55/3.80	2.51/3.73	2.48/3.67	2.43/3.56	2.39/3.48	2.33/3.36	2.29/3.29	2.25/3.20	2.21/3.12	2.18/3.07	2.15/3.00	2.12/2.97	2.10/2.92	2.08/2.89	2.07/2.87	15
16	4.49/8.53	3.63/6.23	3.24/5.29	3.01/4.77	2.85/4.44	2.74/4.20	2.66/4.03	2.59/3.89	2.54/3.78	2.49/3.69	2.45/3.61	2.42/3.55	2.37/3.45	2.33/3.37	2.28/3.25	2.24/3.18	2.20/3.10	2.16/3.01	2.13/2.96	2.09/2.89	2.07/2.86	2.04/2.80	2.02/2.77	2.01/2.75	16
17	4.45/8.40	3.59/6.11	3.20/5.18	2.96/4.67	2.81/4.34	2.70/4.10	2.62/3.93	2.55/3.79	2.50/3.68	2.45/3.59	2.41/3.52	2.38/3.45	2.33/3.35	2.29/3.27	2.23/3.16	2.19/3.08	2.15/3.00	2.11/2.92	2.08/2.86	2.04/2.79	2.02/2.76	1.99/2.70	1.97/2.67	1.96/2.65	17
18	4.41/8.28	3.55/6.01	3.16/5.09	2.93/4.58	2.77/4.25	2.66/4.01	2.58/3.85	2.51/3.71	2.46/3.60	2.41/3.51	2.37/3.44	2.34/3.37	2.29/3.27	2.25/3.19	2.19/3.07	2.15/3.00	2.11/2.91	2.07/2.83	2.04/2.78	2.00/2.71	1.98/2.68	1.95/2.62	1.93/2.59	1.92/2.57	18
19	4.38/8.18	3.52/5.93	3.13/5.01	2.90/4.50	2.74/4.17	2.63/3.94	2.55/3.77	2.48/3.63	2.43/3.52	2.38/3.43	2.34/3.36	2.31/3.30	2.26/3.19	2.21/3.12	2.15/3.00	2.11/2.92	2.07/2.84	2.02/2.76	2.00/2.70	1.96/2.63	1.94/2.60	1.91/2.54	1.90/2.51	1.88/2.49	19
20	4.35/8.10	3.49/5.85	3.10/4.94	2.87/4.43	2.71/4.10	2.60/3.87	2.52/3.71	2.45/3.56	2.40/3.45	2.35/3.37	2.31/3.30	2.28/3.23	2.23/3.13	2.18/3.05	2.12/2.94	2.08/2.86	2.04/2.77	1.99/2.69	1.96/2.63	1.92/2.56	1.90/2.53	1.87/2.47	1.85/2.44	1.84/2.42	20
21	4.32/8.02	3.47/5.78	3.07/4.87	2.84/4.37	2.68/4.04	2.57/3.81	2.49/3.65	2.42/3.51	2.37/3.40	2.32/3.31	2.28/3.24	2.25/3.17	2.20/3.07	2.15/2.99	2.09/2.88	2.05/2.80	2.00/2.72	1.96/2.63	1.93/2.58	1.89/2.51	1.87/2.47	1.84/2.42	1.82/2.38	1.81/2.36	21
22	4.30/7.94	3.44/5.72	3.05/4.82	2.82/4.31	2.66/3.99	2.55/3.76	2.47/3.59	2.40/3.45	2.35/3.35	2.30/3.26	2.26/3.18	2.23/3.12	2.18/3.02	2.13/2.94	2.07/2.83	2.03/2.75	1.98/2.67	1.93/2.58	1.91/2.53	1.87/2.46	1.84/2.42	1.81/2.37	1.80/2.33	1.78/2.31	22
23	4.28/7.88	3.42/5.66	3.03/4.76	2.80/4.26	2.64/3.94	2.53/3.71	2.45/3.54	2.38/3.41	2.32/3.30	2.28/3.21	2.24/3.14	2.20/3.07	2.14/2.97	2.10/2.89	2.04/2.78	2.00/2.70	1.96/2.62	1.91/2.53	1.88/2.48	1.84/2.41	1.82/2.37	1.79/2.32	1.77/2.28	1.76/2.26	23
24	4.26/7.82	3.40/5.61	3.01/4.72	2.78/4.22	2.62/3.90	2.51/3.67	2.43/3.50	2.36/3.36	2.30/3.25	2.26/3.17	2.22/3.09	2.18/3.03	2.13/2.93	2.09/2.85	2.02/2.74	1.98/2.66	1.94/2.58	1.89/2.49	1.86/2.44	1.82/2.36	1.80/2.33	1.76/2.27	1.74/2.23	1.73/2.21	24
25	4.24/7.77	3.38/5.57	2.99/4.68	2.76/4.18	2.60/3.86	2.49/3.63	2.41/3.46	2.34/3.32	2.28/3.21	2.24/3.13	2.20/3.05	2.16/2.99	2.11/2.89	2.06/2.81	2.00/2.70	1.96/2.62	1.92/2.54	1.87/2.45	1.84/2.40	1.80/2.32	1.77/2.29	1.74/2.23	1.72/2.19	1.71/2.17	25
26	4.22/7.72	3.37/5.53	2.98/4.64	2.74/4.14	2.59/3.82	2.47/3.59	2.39/3.42	2.32/3.29	2.27/3.17	2.22/3.09	2.18/3.02	2.15/2.96	2.10/2.86	2.05/2.77	1.99/2.66	1.95/2.58	1.90/2.50	1.85/2.41	1.82/2.36	1.78/2.28	1.76/2.25	1.72/2.19	1.70/2.15	1.69/2.13	26

n₁ degrees of freedom (for greater mean square)

n_2	1	2	3	4	5	6	7	8	9	10	11	12	14	16	20	24	30	40	50	75	100	200	500	∞	n_2
27	4.21 7.68	3.35 5.49	2.96 4.60	2.73 4.11	2.57 3.79	2.46 3.56	2.37 3.39	2.30 3.26	2.25 3.14	2.20 3.06	2.16 2.98	2.13 2.93	2.08 2.83	2.03 2.74	1.97 2.63	1.93 2.55	1.88 2.47	1.84 2.38	1.80 2.33	1.76 2.25	1.74 2.21	1.71 2.16	1.68 2.12	1.67 2.10	27
28	4.20 7.64	3.34 5.45	2.95 4.57	2.71 4.07	2.56 3.76	2.44 3.53	2.36 3.36	2.29 3.23	2.24 3.11	2.19 3.03	2.15 2.95	2.12 2.90	2.06 2.80	2.02 2.71	1.96 2.60	1.91 2.52	1.87 2.44	1.81 2.35	1.78 2.30	1.75 2.22	1.72 2.18	1.69 2.13	1.67 2.09	1.65 2.06	28
29	4.18 7.60	3.33 5.42	2.93 4.54	2.70 4.04	2.54 3.73	2.43 3.50	2.35 3.33	2.28 3.20	2.22 3.08	2.18 3.00	2.14 2.92	2.10 2.87	2.05 2.77	2.00 2.68	1.94 2.57	1.90 2.49	1.85 2.41	1.80 2.32	1.77 2.27	1.73 2.19	1.71 2.15	1.68 2.10	1.65 2.06	1.64 2.03	29
30	4.17 7.56	3.32 5.39	2.92 4.51	2.69 4.02	2.53 3.70	2.42 3.47	2.34 3.30	2.27 3.17	2.21 3.06	2.16 2.98	2.12 2.90	2.09 2.84	2.04 2.74	1.99 2.66	1.93 2.55	1.89 2.47	1.84 2.38	1.79 2.29	1.76 2.24	1.72 2.16	1.69 2.13	1.66 2.07	1.64 2.03	1.62 2.01	30
32	4.15 7.50	3.30 5.34	2.90 4.46	2.67 3.97	2.51 3.66	2.40 3.42	2.32 3.25	2.25 3.12	2.19 3.01	2.14 2.94	2.10 2.86	2.07 2.80	2.02 2.70	1.97 2.62	1.91 2.51	1.86 2.42	1.82 2.34	1.76 2.25	1.74 2.20	1.69 2.12	1.67 2.08	1.64 2.02	1.61 1.98	1.59 1.96	32
34	4.13 7.44	3.28 5.29	2.88 4.42	2.65 3.93	2.49 3.61	2.38 3.38	2.30 3.21	2.23 3.08	2.17 2.97	2.12 2.89	2.08 2.82	2.05 2.76	2.00 2.66	1.95 2.58	1.89 2.47	1.84 2.38	1.80 2.30	1.74 2.21	1.71 2.15	1.67 2.08	1.64 2.04	1.61 1.98	1.59 1.94	1.57 1.91	34
36	4.11 7.39	3.26 5.25	2.86 4.38	2.63 3.89	2.48 3.58	2.36 3.35	2.28 3.18	2.21 3.04	2.15 2.94	2.10 2.86	2.06 2.78	2.03 2.72	1.98 2.62	1.93 2.54	1.87 2.43	1.82 2.35	1.78 2.26	1.72 2.17	1.69 2.12	1.65 2.04	1.62 2.00	1.59 1.94	1.56 1.90	1.55 1.87	36
38	4.10 7.35	3.25 5.21	2.85 4.34	2.62 3.86	2.46 3.54	2.35 3.32	2.26 3.15	2.19 3.02	2.14 2.91	2.09 2.82	2.05 2.75	2.02 2.69	1.96 2.59	1.92 2.51	1.85 2.40	1.80 2.32	1.76 2.22	1.71 2.14	1.67 2.08	1.63 2.00	1.60 1.97	1.57 1.90	1.54 1.86	1.53 1.84	38
40	4.08 7.31	3.23 5.18	2.84 4.31	2.61 3.83	2.45 3.51	2.34 3.29	2.25 3.12	2.18 2.99	2.12 2.88	2.07 2.80	2.04 2.73	2.00 2.66	1.95 2.56	1.90 2.49	1.84 2.37	1.79 2.29	1.74 2.20	1.69 2.11	1.66 2.05	1.61 1.97	1.59 1.94	1.55 1.88	1.53 1.84	1.51 1.81	40
42	4.07 7.27	3.22 5.15	2.83 4.29	2.59 3.80	2.44 3.49	2.32 3.26	2.24 3.10	2.17 2.96	2.11 2.86	2.06 2.77	2.02 2.70	1.99 2.64	1.94 2.54	1.89 2.46	1.82 2.35	1.78 2.26	1.73 2.17	1.68 2.08	1.64 2.02	1.60 1.94	1.57 1.91	1.54 1.85	1.51 1.80	1.49 1.78	42
44	4.06 7.24	3.21 5.12	2.82 4.26	2.58 3.78	2.43 3.46	2.31 3.24	2.23 3.07	2.16 2.94	2.10 2.84	2.05 2.75	2.01 2.68	1.98 2.62	1.92 2.52	1.88 2.44	1.81 2.32	1.76 2.24	1.72 2.15	1.66 2.06	1.63 2.00	1.58 1.92	1.56 1.88	1.52 1.82	1.50 1.78	1.48 1.75	44
46	4.05 7.21	3.20 5.10	2.81 4.24	2.57 3.76	2.42 3.44	2.30 3.22	2.22 3.05	2.14 2.92	2.09 2.82	2.04 2.73	2.00 2.66	1.97 2.60	1.91 2.50	1.87 2.42	1.80 2.30	1.75 2.22	1.71 2.13	1.65 2.04	1.62 1.98	1.57 1.90	1.54 1.86	1.51 1.80	1.48 1.76	1.46 1.72	46
48	4.04 7.19	3.19 5.08	2.80 4.22	2.56 3.74	2.41 3.42	2.30 3.20	2.21 3.04	2.14 2.90	2.08 2.80	2.03 2.71	1.99 2.64	1.96 2.58	1.90 2.48	1.86 2.40	1.79 2.28	1.74 2.20	1.70 2.11	1.64 2.02	1.61 1.96	1.56 1.88	1.53 1.84	1.50 1.78	1.47 1.73	1.45 1.70	48

n_1 degrees of freedom (for greater mean square)

n_2	1	2	3	4	5	6	7	8	9	10	11	12	14	16	20	24	30	40	50	75	100	200	500	∞
50	4.03 / 7.17	3.18 / 5.06	2.79 / 4.20	2.56 / 3.72	2.40 / 3.41	2.29 / 3.18	2.20 / 3.02	2.13 / 2.88	2.07 / 2.78	2.02 / 2.70	1.98 / 2.62	1.95 / 2.56	1.90 / 2.46	1.85 / 2.39	1.78 / 2.26	1.74 / 2.18	1.69 / 2.10	1.63 / 2.00	1.60 / 1.94	1.55 / 1.86	1.52 / 1.82	1.48 / 1.76	1.46 / 1.71	1.44 / 1.68
55	4.02 / 7.12	3.17 / 5.01	2.78 / 4.16	2.54 / 3.68	2.38 / 3.37	2.27 / 3.15	2.18 / 2.98	2.11 / 2.85	2.05 / 2.75	2.00 / 2.66	1.97 / 2.59	1.93 / 2.53	1.88 / 2.43	1.83 / 2.35	1.76 / 2.23	1.72 / 2.15	1.67 / 2.06	1.61 / 1.96	1.58 / 1.90	1.52 / 1.82	1.50 / 1.78	1.46 / 1.71	1.43 / 1.66	1.41 / 1.64
60	4.00 / 7.08	3.15 / 4.98	2.76 / 4.13	2.52 / 3.65	2.37 / 3.34	2.25 / 3.12	2.17 / 2.95	2.10 / 2.82	2.04 / 2.72	1.99 / 2.63	1.95 / 2.56	1.92 / 2.50	1.86 / 2.40	1.81 / 2.32	1.75 / 2.20	1.70 / 2.12	1.65 / 2.03	1.59 / 1.93	1.56 / 1.87	1.50 / 1.79	1.48 / 1.74	1.44 / 1.68	1.41 / 1.63	1.39 / 1.60
65	3.99 / 7.04	3.14 / 4.95	2.75 / 4.10	2.51 / 3.62	2.36 / 3.31	2.24 / 3.09	2.15 / 2.93	2.08 / 2.79	2.02 / 2.70	1.98 / 2.61	1.94 / 2.54	1.90 / 2.47	1.85 / 2.37	1.80 / 2.30	1.73 / 2.18	1.68 / 2.09	1.63 / 2.00	1.57 / 1.90	1.54 / 1.84	1.49 / 1.76	1.46 / 1.71	1.42 / 1.64	1.39 / 1.60	1.37 / 1.56
70	3.98 / 7.01	3.13 / 4.92	2.74 / 4.08	2.50 / 3.60	2.35 / 3.29	2.23 / 3.07	2.14 / 2.91	2.07 / 2.77	2.01 / 2.67	1.97 / 2.59	1.93 / 2.51	1.89 / 2.45	1.84 / 2.35	1.79 / 2.28	1.72 / 2.15	1.67 / 2.07	1.62 / 1.98	1.56 / 1.88	1.53 / 1.82	1.47 / 1.74	1.45 / 1.69	1.40 / 1.62	1.37 / 1.56	1.35 / 1.53
80	3.96 / 6.96	3.11 / 4.88	2.72 / 4.04	2.48 / 3.56	2.33 / 3.25	2.21 / 3.04	2.12 / 2.87	2.05 / 2.74	1.99 / 2.64	1.95 / 2.55	1.91 / 2.48	1.88 / 2.41	1.82 / 2.32	1.77 / 2.24	1.70 / 2.11	1.65 / 2.03	1.60 / 1.94	1.54 / 1.84	1.51 / 1.78	1.45 / 1.70	1.42 / 1.65	1.38 / 1.57	1.35 / 1.52	1.32 / 1.49
100	3.94 / 6.90	3.09 / 4.82	2.70 / 3.98	2.46 / 3.51	2.30 / 3.20	2.19 / 2.99	2.10 / 2.82	2.03 / 2.69	1.97 / 2.59	1.92 / 2.51	1.88 / 2.43	1.85 / 2.36	1.79 / 2.26	1.75 / 2.19	1.68 / 2.06	1.63 / 1.98	1.57 / 1.89	1.51 / 1.79	1.48 / 1.73	1.42 / 1.64	1.39 / 1.59	1.34 / 1.51	1.30 / 1.46	1.28 / 1.43
125	3.92 / 6.84	3.07 / 4.78	2.68 / 3.94	2.44 / 3.47	2.29 / 3.17	2.17 / 2.95	2.08 / 2.79	2.01 / 2.65	1.95 / 2.56	1.90 / 2.47	1.86 / 2.40	1.83 / 2.33	1.77 / 2.23	1.72 / 2.15	1.65 / 2.03	1.60 / 1.94	1.55 / 1.85	1.49 / 1.75	1.45 / 1.68	1.39 / 1.59	1.36 / 1.54	1.31 / 1.46	1.27 / 1.40	1.25 / 1.37
150	3.91 / 6.81	3.06 / 4.75	2.67 / 3.91	2.43 / 3.44	2.27 / 3.14	2.16 / 2.92	2.07 / 2.76	2.00 / 2.62	1.94 / 2.53	1.89 / 2.44	1.85 / 2.37	1.82 / 2.30	1.76 / 2.20	1.71 / 2.12	1.64 / 2.00	1.59 / 1.91	1.54 / 1.83	1.47 / 1.72	1.44 / 1.66	1.37 / 1.56	1.34 / 1.51	1.29 / 1.43	1.25 / 1.37	1.22 / 1.33
200	3.89 / 6.76	3.04 / 4.71	2.65 / 3.88	2.41 / 3.41	2.26 / 3.11	2.14 / 2.90	2.05 / 2.73	1.98 / 2.60	1.92 / 2.50	1.87 / 2.41	1.83 / 2.34	1.80 / 2.28	1.74 / 2.17	1.69 / 2.09	1.62 / 1.97	1.57 / 1.88	1.52 / 1.79	1.45 / 1.69	1.42 / 1.62	1.35 / 1.53	1.32 / 1.48	1.26 / 1.39	1.22 / 1.33	1.19 / 1.28
400	3.86 / 6.70	3.02 / 4.66	2.62 / 3.83	2.39 / 3.36	2.23 / 3.06	2.12 / 2.85	2.03 / 2.69	1.96 / 2.55	1.90 / 2.46	1.85 / 2.37	1.81 / 2.29	1.78 / 2.23	1.72 / 2.12	1.67 / 2.04	1.60 / 1.92	1.54 / 1.84	1.49 / 1.74	1.42 / 1.64	1.38 / 1.57	1.32 / 1.47	1.28 / 1.42	1.22 / 1.32	1.16 / 1.24	1.13 / 1.19
1000	3.85 / 6.66	3.00 / 4.62	2.61 / 3.80	2.38 / 3.34	2.22 / 3.04	2.10 / 2.82	2.02 / 2.66	1.95 / 2.53	1.89 / 2.43	1.84 / 2.34	1.80 / 2.26	1.76 / 2.20	1.70 / 2.09	1.65 / 2.01	1.58 / 1.89	1.53 / 1.81	1.47 / 1.71	1.41 / 1.61	1.36 / 1.54	1.30 / 1.44	1.26 / 1.38	1.19 / 1.28	1.13 / 1.19	1.08 / 1.11
∞	3.84 / 6.64	2.99 / 4.60	2.60 / 3.78	2.37 / 3.32	2.21 / 3.02	2.09 / 2.80	2.01 / 2.64	1.94 / 2.51	1.88 / 2.41	1.83 / 2.32	1.79 / 2.24	1.75 / 2.18	1.69 / 2.07	1.64 / 1.99	1.57 / 1.87	1.52 / 1.79	1.46 / 1.69	1.40 / 1.59	1.35 / 1.52	1.28 / 1.41	1.24 / 1.36	1.17 / 1.25	1.11 / 1.15	1.00 / 1.00

APPENDIX II

This Appendix is presented for those readers who may be interested in some of the more technical aspects of the coefficient of intraclass correlation, and in its relation to other statistical procedures and tests. The proofs referred to in the text are given below.[1]

A. HARRIS' FORMULA FOR R (SEE P. 10)

Harris' (1913) formula, which is given as formula **1** in the text, is

$$kS_c^2 = S^2\{1 + (k - 1)R\}$$

where $S^2 = \dfrac{1}{ck} \sum_i^c \sum_j^k (X_{ij} - \bar{X})^2 = $ variance of the total set of scores,

$Sc^2 = \dfrac{1}{c} \sum_i^c (\bar{X}_i - \bar{X})^2 = $ variance of class means,

$k = $ number of members in each class,

$c = $ number of classes,

$X_{ij} = $ score of the jth member in the ith class,

$\bar{X}_i = $ mean of the ith class, and

$\bar{X} = $ mean of the total set of scores (or grand mean).

---

[1] These proofs were provided by Dr. Hari C. Gupta in connection with his work on the USPHS Project M-912; they are also given in essentially the same form in Dr. Gupta's dissertation (1955). Some of the symbols in this appendix differ slightly from those in the text. For example, the symbol used here for the total sums of squares is S_T, whereas the corresponding designation in Table 1 is total SS, and in the case of ranks is TSS_r, as seen in Chapter VIII, formula **21**.

However, the value of R estimated from the above formula is somewhat biased. In order to show the extent and nature of the bias we shall introduce the following notation:

$$S_T = \sum_i^c \sum_j^k (X_{ij} - \bar{X})^2 = \text{total sum of squares}$$

$$S_B = k \sum_i^c (\bar{X}_i - \bar{X})^2 = \text{sum of squares for variation between classes}$$

$$S_W = S_T - S_B = \text{sum of squares for variation within classes}$$

$$BCMS = \frac{S_B}{c - 1} = \text{between-classes mean square}$$

$$WMS = \frac{S_W}{c(k - 1)} = \text{within-classes mean square.}$$

Formula **1** may then be presented in terms of the mean squares of the analysis of variance table. Rewriting formula **1** in raw score form, we have

$$k \frac{1}{c} \sum_i^c (\bar{X}_i - \bar{X})^2 = \frac{1}{ck} \sum_i^c \sum_j^k (X_{ij} - \bar{X})^2 \{1 + (k - 1)R\}$$

or, multiplying each side by c, we get

$$S_B = \frac{1}{k} S_T \{1 + (k - 1)R\}$$

whence

$$R = \frac{1}{k - 1} \left\{ \frac{kS_B}{S_T} - 1 \right\}$$

Using the relation $S_T = S_B + S_W$,

$$R = \frac{1}{k - 1} \left\{ \frac{kS_B - S_B - S_W}{S_B + S_W} \right\}$$

which reduces to

$$R = \frac{(k - 1)S_B - S_W}{(k - 1)(S_B + S_W)}$$

Dividing the numerator and the denominator in the above by $c(k-1)$,

$$R = \frac{S_B/c - S_W/[c(k-1)]}{S_B/c + [(k-1)S_W]/[c(k-1)]}$$

$$= \frac{BCMS^* - WMS}{BCMS^* + (k-1)WMS} = R_H$$

which is formula **1'** in the text.

B. THE RELATION OF R_H TO $\bar{r}$ (SEE PROPERTY 6 OF R, P. 26)

Without loss of generality, we can consider simply the deviations of scores from the grand mean. Therefore let x_{ij} be the deviation of the score x_{ij} in the ith row and the jth column from the grand mean; then, since all the column means are equal, the x_{ij}'s are also the deviations from their respective column means for each j fixed. Then taking (j, l) and (l, j) as different pairs of columns, there are in all $k(k-1)$ such pairs. Hence

$$\bar{r} = \frac{1}{k(k-1)} \cdot \sum_{i=1}^{c} \sum_{j=1}^{k} \frac{\sum_{i=1}^{c} x_{ij} x_{il}}{\sqrt{\sum_{i}^{c} x_{ij}^2} \sqrt{\sum_{i}^{c} x_{il}^2}}, \qquad l \neq j$$

The numerator may be written

$$\sum_{i}^{c} \left(\sum_{j}^{k} x_{ij} \right)^2 - \sum_{i}^{c} \sum_{j}^{k} x_{ij}^2 = kS_B - S_T$$

Also, since the k variances are assumed to be equal,

$$\sum_{i}^{c} x_{ij}^2 = \sum_{i}^{c} x_{il}^2$$

so that the denominator may be written

$$\frac{1}{k} \sum_{j}^{k} \sum_{i}^{c} x_{ij}^2 = \frac{1}{k} S_T$$

Therefore

$$\bar{r} = \frac{1}{k(k-1)} \cdot \frac{kS_B - S_T}{(1/k)S_T}$$

But $S_T = S_B + S_W$. Therefore, substituting $S_B + S_W$ for S_T, we get

$$\bar{r} = \frac{1}{k(k-1)} \cdot \frac{kS_B - S_B - S_W}{(1/k)(S_B + S_W)} = \frac{(k-1)S_B - S_W}{(k-1)(S_B + S_W)}$$

Dividing the numerator and the denominator by $c(k-1)$,

$$\bar{r} = \frac{\dfrac{S_B}{c} - \dfrac{S_W}{c(k-1)}}{\dfrac{S_B}{c} + \dfrac{(k-1)S_W}{c(k-1)}} = \frac{BCMS^* - WMS}{BCMS^* + (k-1)WMS} = R_H$$

C. THE RELATION OF R_c TO $\bar{r}$ (SEE PROPERTY 7 OF R, P. 28)

Again, without loss of generality, we can consider simply the deviations of scores from the mean of their respective columns. This amounts to equating column means arithmetically. Let x_{ij}' be the deviation of the score X_{ij} in the ith row and the jth column from $\bar{X}_j$, the mean of the jth column. Considering the $c \times k$ matrix of the x_{ij}''s, all column means are zero and so is the grand mean; so that x_{ij}''s are also the deviations from the grand mean. The sum of squares between column means (S_k) is zero and so is the correction factor. The analysis of variance table will then take the following form:

Source of Variation	SS	df	MS
Between classes	S_B	$c - 1$	BCMS
Within classes	S_W'	$(c-1)(k-1)$	RMS
Between columns	$S_k = 0$	$k - 1$	BKMS
Total	S_T	$ck - 1$	

Then

$$\bar{r} = \frac{1}{k(k-1)} \cdot \sum_{l=1}^{c} \sum_{j=1}^{k} \frac{\sum\limits_{i=1}^{c} x_{ij}' \, x_{il}'}{\sqrt{\sum\limits_{i}^{c} x_{ij}'^2} \sqrt{\sum\limits_{i}^{c} x_{il}'^2}}, \quad l \neq j$$

The numerator may be written

$$\sum_{i}^{c}\left(\sum_{j}^{k} x_{ij}'\right)^2 - \sum_{i}^{c} \sum_{j}^{k} x_{ij}'^2 = kS_B - S_T$$

Also, since the k variances are assumed to be equal,

$$\sum_{i}^{c} x_{ij}'^2 = \sum_{i}^{c} x_{il}'^2$$

so that the denominator may be written

$$\frac{1}{k} \sum_{j}^{k} \sum_{i}^{c} x_{ij}'^2 = \frac{1}{k} S_T$$

Therefore

$$\bar{r} = \frac{1}{k(k-1)} \cdot \frac{kS_B - S_T}{(1/k)S_T}$$

But $S_T = S_B + S_W' + S_k$, where $S_k = 0$. Therefore, substituting $S_B + S_W'$ for S_T, we get

$$\bar{r} = \frac{1}{k(k-1)} \cdot \frac{kS_B - S_B - S_W'}{(1/k)(S_B + S_W')} = \frac{(k-1)S_B - S_W'}{(k-1)(S_B + S_W')}$$

Dividing the numerator and the denominator by $(c-1)(k-1)$,

$$\bar{r} = \frac{\dfrac{S_B}{c-1} - \dfrac{S_W'}{(c-1)(k-1)}}{\dfrac{S_B}{c-1} + \dfrac{(k-1)S_W'}{(c-1)(k-1)}} = \frac{BCMS - RMS}{BCMS + (k-1)RMS} = R_c$$

D. THE RELATION OF R_f TO R_c (SEE P. 38)

The values of R_f and R_c are given by the formulas

$$R_f = \frac{BCMS - WMS}{BCMS + (k-1)WMS} \qquad \text{(formula 2)}$$

$$R_c = \frac{BCMS - RMS}{BCMS + (k-1)RMS} \qquad \text{(formula 8)}$$

It is evident from the above formulas that, other factors being equal, the value of the coefficient of intraclass correlation decreases as the residual mean square increases, because any increase in the RMS decreases the numerator and increases the denominator of the formula for R. Thus

$R_c \gtreqless R_f$ according as $BKMS \gtreqless RMS$

$$\text{or} \quad \frac{BKMS(k-1) + RMS(c-1)(k-1)}{c(k-1)} \gtreqless RMS$$

$$\text{or} \quad BKMS \gtreqless RMS$$

$$\text{or} \quad \frac{BKMS}{RMS} \gtreqless 1$$

$$\text{or} \quad F_k \gtreqless 1$$

Therefore the effect of equalizing the k column means is

to raise R if $F_k > 1$

to lower R if $F_k < 1$

and R remains unaffected if $F_k = 1$.

E. R FOR THE THREE-PARAMETER CASE (SEE P. 77)

When $k = 2$, R_H is equal to the maximum likelihood estimate of ρ, in the case of samples from populations specified by three parameters, viz., $\mu_1 = \mu_2 = \mu$; $\sigma_1 = \sigma_2 = \sigma$; ρ_{xy}.

Let X_i, Y_i be the scores of the ith individual on the first and second trials respectively. Then R_H will be calculated as follows (all sums are over i, where $i = 1, 2, \ldots, c$):

$$C = \text{correction term} = \frac{(\sum X_i + \sum Y_i)^2}{2c}$$

$$S_T = \text{total } SS = \sum X_i^2 + \sum Y_i^2 - C$$

$$S_B = \text{between-individuals } SS = \tfrac{1}{2}\sum[X_i + Y_i]^2 - C, \text{ for } c \ df$$

$$S_W = \text{within-classes } SS = S_T - S_B = \sum X_i^2 + \sum Y_i^2 - \tfrac{1}{2}\sum[X_i + Y_i]^2, \text{ for } c \ df$$

$$S_B - S_W = \sum[X_i + Y_i]^2 - \sum X_i^2 - \sum Y_i^2 - C$$
$$= \sum X_i^2 + \sum Y_i^2 + 2\sum X_i Y_i - \sum X_i^2 - \sum Y_i^2 - C$$
$$= 2\sum X_i Y_i = C$$

$$S_B + S_W = \sum X_i^2 + \sum Y_i^2 - C$$

Now

$$R_H = \frac{BCMS^* - RMS}{BCMS^* + RMS} = \frac{S_B/_c - S_W/_c}{S_B/_c + S_W/_c} = \frac{S_B - S_W}{S_B + S_W}$$

Substituting for $S_B - S_W$, $S_B + S_W$, and C, we get

$$R_H = \frac{2\sum X_i Y_i - (\sum X_i + \sum Y_i)^2/2c}{\sum X_i^2 + \sum Y_i^2 - (\sum X_i + \sum Y_i)^2/2c}$$

which is the maximum likelihood estimate of ρ_{xy} for the three-parameter case.

F. R FOR THE FOUR-PARAMETER CASE (SEE P. 77)

For the case $k = 2$, R_c is equal to the maximum likelihood estimate of ρ in the case of samples from populations specified by four parameters, viz., μ_x; μ_y; $\sigma_x = \sigma_y = \sigma$; ρ_{xy}.

Let X_i, Y_i be the scores of the individual on the first and second trials respectively. Then R_c will be calculated as follows (all sums are over i, where $i = 1, 2, \ldots, c$):

$$C = \text{correction term} = \frac{(\sum X_i + \sum Y_i)^2}{2c}$$

$$= \frac{(\sum X_i)^2}{2c} + \frac{(\sum Y_i)^2}{2c} + \frac{2(\sum X_i)(\sum Y_i)}{2c}$$

$$S_T = \text{total } SS = \sum X_i^2 + \sum Y_i^2 - C$$

$$S_B = \text{between-individuals } SS = \frac{1}{2} \sum [X_i + Y_i]^2 - C, \text{ for } c - 1 \ df$$

$$S_k = \text{between-trials } SS = \frac{1}{c}[(\sum X_i)^2 + (\sum Y_i)^2] - C, \text{ for } 1 \ df$$

$$S_W' = \text{residual } SS = S_T - S_B - S_k$$

$$= \sum X_i^2 + \sum Y_i^2 - \frac{1}{2} \sum [X_i + Y_i]^2 - \frac{1}{c}[(\sum X_i)^2 + (\sum Y_i)^2] + C, \text{ for } c - 1 \ df$$

$$S_B - S_W' = \sum [X_i + Y_i]^2 - \sum X_i^2 - \sum Y_i^2 + \frac{1}{c}[(\sum X_i)^2 + (\sum Y_i)^2] - 2C$$

Expanding the first term and substituting for $2C$, we get

$$S_B - S_W' = \sum X_i^2 + \sum Y_i^2 + 2\sum X_i Y_i - \sum X_i^2 - \sum Y_i^2$$
$$+ \frac{1}{c}[(\sum X_i)^2 + (\sum Y_i)^2 - (\sum X_i)^2 - (\sum Y_i)^2 - 2(\sum X_i)(\sum Y_i)]$$

$$= 2\sum X_i Y_i - \frac{2}{c}(\sum X_i)(\sum Y_i)$$

$$S_B + S_W' = S_T - S_k = \sum X_i^2 - \frac{(\sum X_i)^2}{c} + \sum Y_i^2 - \frac{(\sum Y_i)^2}{c}$$

Now

$$R_c = \frac{BCMS - RMS}{BCMS + RMS} = \frac{S_B/(c-1) - S_W'/(c-1)}{S_B/(c-1) + S_W'/(c-1)}$$

$$= \frac{S_B - S_W'}{S_B + S_W'}$$

Substituting for $S_B - S_W'$ and $S_B + S_W'$, we get

$$R_c = \frac{2\left[\sum X_i Y_i - \dfrac{(\sum X_i)(\sum Y_i)}{c}\right]}{\left[\sum X_i^2 - \dfrac{(\sum X_i)^2}{c}\right] + \left[\sum Y_i^2 - \dfrac{(\sum Y_i)^2}{c}\right]}$$

which is the maximum likelihood (also unbiased) estimate of ρ_{xy} for the four-parameter case.

REFERENCES

Alexander, H. W. (1946) A general test for trend. *Psychol. Bull.*, 43, 553–557.

Alexander, H. W. (1947) The estimation of reliability when several trials are available. *Psychometrika*, 12, 79–99.

Anderson, R. L., and Bancroft, T. A. (1952) *Statistical theory in research.* New York: McGraw-Hill.

Benard, A., and Elteren, Ph. van. (1953) A generalization of the method of *m* rankings. *Koninklijke Nederlandse Akademie van Wetenschappen. Proceedings, Series A*, 56, 358–369.

Bhargava, R. P. (1946) Test of significance for intraclass correlation when family sizes are not equal. *Sankhyā*, 7, 435–438.

Blair, G. M. (1949) The content of educational psychology. *J. educ. Psychol.*, 40, 267–274.

Block, J., Levine, L., and McNemar, Q. (1951) Testing for the existence of psychometric patterns. *J. abn., soc. Psychol.*, 46, 356–359.

Boas, F. (1916) On the variety of lines of descent represented in a population. *Amer. Anthropologist*, 18, 1–9.

Bock, R. D. (1956) The selection of judges for preference testing. *Psychometrika*, 21, 349–366.

Bock, R. D., and Haggard, E. A. The use of canonical analysis in the study of individual differences. (Unpublished paper.)

Brown, W. (1910) Some experimental results in the correlation of mental abilities. *Brit. J. Psychol.*, 3, 296–322.

Brozek, J., Simonson, E., Bushard, W. J., and Peterson, J. H. (1948) Effects of practice and the consistency of repeated measurements of accommodation and vergence. *Am. J. Ophthalmology*, 31, 191–198.

Brunswik, E. (1956) *Perception and the representative design of psychological experiments.* Berkeley: Univ. of California Press.

Burt, C. (1955) Test reliability by analysis of variance. *Brit. J. statist. Psychol.*, 8, 103–118.

Cattell, R. B. (1949) r_p and other coefficients of pattern similarity. *Psychometrika*, 14, 279–289.

Cochran, W. G. (1951) Testing a linear relation among variances. *Biometrics*, 7, 17–32.

157

Cochran, W. G. (1953) *Sampling techniques.* New York: Wiley.

Coombs, C. H. (1948) The role of correlation in analysis of variance. *Psychometrika,* 13, 233–243.

Cronbach, L. J. (1947) Test "reliability": its meaning and determination. *Psychometrika,* 12, 1–16.

Cronbach, L. J. (1949) *Essentials of psychological testing.* New York: Harper & Bros.

Cronbach, L. J. (1951) Coefficient alpha and the internal structure of tests. *Psychometrika,* 16, 297–334.

Cronbach, L. J., and Gleser, G. C. (1953) Assessing similarity between profiles. *Psychol. Bull.,* 50, 456–473.

Crump, S. L. (1946) The estimation of variance components in analysis of variance. *Biometrics Bull.,* 2, 7–11.

Crump, S. L. (1951) The present status of variance component analysis. *Biometrics,* 7, 1–16.

Danford, M. B. (1955) Some mathematical statistical approaches to pattern analysis. *Symposium on pattern analysis.* USAF School of Aviation Medicine, Randolph Field, pp. 15–28.

Daniels, H. E. (1939) The estimation of components of variance. *J. Roy. Stat. Soc., Suppl.* 6, 186–197.

Derner, G. F., Aborn, M., and Canter, A. H. (1950) The reliability of the Wechsler-Bellevue subtests and scales. *J. consult. Psychol.,* 14, 172–179.

du Mas, F. M. (1949) The coefficient of profile similarity. *J. clin. Psychol.,* 5, 123–131.

Durbin, J. (1951) Incomplete blocks in ranking experiments. *Brit. J. Psychol. (Statist. Sec.),* 4, 85–94.

Ebel, R. L. (1951) Estimation of the reliability of ratings. *Psychometrika,* 16, 407–424.

Edwards, A. L. (1954a) *Statistical methods for the behavioral sciences.* New York: Rinehart.

Edwards, A. L. (1954b) *Manual: Edwards personal preference schedule.* New York: Psychological Corporation.

Ehrenberg, A. S. C. (1952) On sampling from a population of rankers. *Biometrika,* 39, 82–87.

Eisenhart, C. (1947) The assumptions underlying the analysis of variance. *Biometrics,* 3, 1–21.

Ellson, D. G. (1947) A method for identifying pattern clusters in test score profiles. *Amer. Psychologist,* 2, 425(a).

Ferguson, G. A. (1941) *The reliability of mental tests.* London: Univ. of London Press.

Fieller, E. C., and Smith, C. A. B. (1951–52) Note on the analysis of variance and intraclass correlation. *Ann. Eugenics,* 16, 97–104.

Fisher, R. A. (1936) "The coefficient of racial likeness" and the future of craniometry. *J. Roy. Anthropol. Instit.,* 66, 57–63.

Fisher, R. A. (1950) *Statistical methods for research workers* (*Eleventh ed.*). London: Oliver & Boyd.

Fisher, R. A., and Yates, F. (1953) *Statistical tables for biological, agricultural, and medical research* (*Fourth ed.*). New York: Hafner, 1953.

Fraser, D. A. S. (1957) *Nonparametric methods in statistics*. New York: Wiley.

Friedman, M. (1937) The use of ranks to avoid the assumption of normality implicit in the analysis of variance. *J. Amer. Statist. Assn.*, 32, 657–701.

Friedman, M. (1940) A comparison of alternative tests of significance for the problem of *m* rankings. *Ann. math. Statist.*, 11, 86–92.

Gaier, E. L., and Lee, M. C. (1953) Pattern analysis: The configural approach to predictive measurement. *Psychol. Bull.*, 50, 140–148.

Glaser, R. (1950) Multiple operation measurement. *Psychol. Rev.*, 57, 241–253.

Glaser, R. (1951) The application of the concepts of multiple operation measurement to the response patterns on psychological tests. *Educ., Psychol. Meas.*, 11, 372–382.

Gough, H. G. (1956) *Operational manual for the California Psychological Inventory*. Palo Alto, Calif.: The Consulting Psychologists Press.

Gulliksen, H. (1950) *Theory of mental tests*. New York: Wiley.

Gupta, H. C. (1955) Intraclass correlation in educational research: an exploratory study into some of the possible uses of the technique of intraclass correlation in educational research. Unpubl. Ph.D. Dissertation, Univ. of Chicago.

Guttman, L. (1945) A basis for analyzing test-retest reliability. *Psychometrika*, 10, 255–282.

Haggard, E. A. (1949) On the application of analysis of variance to GSR data: I. The selection of an appropriate measure. *J. exp. Psychol.*, 39, 378–392.

Haggard, E. A. (1953) Techniques for the development of unbiased tests. *Proceedings, 1952 Invitational Conference on Testing Problems*. Princeton, N. J.: Educational Testing Service, pp. 93–120.

Haggard, E. A. (1954) Social-status and intelligence: an experimental study of certain cultural determinants of measured intelligence. *Genet. Psychol. Monogr.*, 49, 141–186.

Haggard, E. A., and Chapman, J. Intraclass correlation vs. factor analysis for determining groups of persons. (In preparation.)

Hald, A. (1952a) *Statistical theory with engineering applications*. New York: Wiley.

Hald, A. (1952b) *Statistical tables and formulas*. New York: Wiley.

Hansen, M. H., and Hurwitz, W. N. (1943) On the theory of sampling from finite populations. *Ann. math. Statist.*, 14, 333–362.

Hansen, M. H., Hurwitz, W. N., Marks, E. S., and Mauldin, W. P. (1951) Response errors in surveys. *J. Amer. Statist. Assn.*, 46, 147–190.

Hansen, M. H., Hurwitz, W. N., and Madow, W. G. (1953) *Sample survey methods and theory. Vol. I: Methods and applications.* New York: Wiley.

Harris, J. A. (1913) On the calculation of intraclass and interclass co-efficients of correlation from class moments when the number of possible combinations is large. *Biometrika*, 9, 446–472.

Harris, J. A. (1914) On spurious values of intraclass correlation co-efficients arising from disorderly differentiation within the classes. *Biometrika*, 10, 412–416.

Harris, J. A. (1915) On a criterion of substratum homogeneity (or heterogeneity) in field experiments. *Amer. Naturalist*, 49, 430–454.

Harter, H. L., and Lum, M. D. (1955) *Partially hierarchal models in the analysis of variance.* WADC Technical Report 55–33, Wright Air Development Center.

Holt, S. B. (1952–53) Genetics of dermal ridges: maximization of intra-class correlation for ridge-counts. *Ann. Eugenics*, 17, 293–301.

Horst, P. (1949) A generalized expression for the reliability of measures. *Psychometrika*, 14, 21–31.

Horst, P. (1954) Pattern analysis and configural scoring. *J. clin. Psychol.*, 10, 3–11.

Hotelling, H., and Pabst, M. R. (1936) Rank correlation and tests of significance involving no assumption of normality. *Ann. math. Statist.*, 7, 29–43.

Hoyt, C. (1941) Test reliability obtained by analysis of variance. *Psychometrika*, 6, 153–160.

Jackson, R. W. B. (1939) Reliability of mental tests. *Brit. J. Psychol.*, 29, 262–287.

Jackson, R. W. B., and Ferguson, G. A. (1941) *Studies on the reliability of tests.* Toronto: Univ. of Toronto, Dept. of Educ. Res., Bull. 12.

Jellinek, E. M. (1940) On the use of the intra-class correlation coefficient in the testing of the difference of certain variance ratios. *J. educ. Psychol.*, 31, 60–63.

Johnson, P. O. (1949) *Statistical methods in research.* Englewood Cliffs, N. J.: Prentice-Hall.

Jonckheere, A. R. (1954a) A test of significance for the relation between m rankings and k ranked categories. *Brit. J. statist. Psychol.*, 7, 93–100.

Jonckheere, A. R. (1954b) A distribution-free k-sample test against ordered alternatives. *Biometrika*, 41, 133–145.

Jones, H. E. (1939a) Principles and methods of the adolescent growth study. *J. consult. Psychol.*, 3, 157–159.

Jones, H. E. (1939b) Procedures of the adolescent growth study. *J. consult. Psychol.*, 3, 177–180.

Jones, M. C. (1948) Adolescent friendships. *Amer. Psychologist*, 3, 352(a).

Kelley, T. L. (1923) *Statistical Method.* New York: Macmillan.

Kempthorne, O. (1952) *Design and analysis of experiments.* New York: Wiley.

Kendall, M. G., and Smith, B. B. (1939) The problem of m rankings. *Ann. math. Statist.*, 10, 275–287.

Kendall, M. G. (1945) The treatment of ties in ranking problems. *Biometrika*, 33, 239–251.

Kendall, M. G. (1949) On the reconciliation of theories of probability. *Biometrika*, 36, 101–116.

Kendall, M. G. (1951) *The advanced theory of statistics (Vol. II)*. New York: Hafner.

Kendall, M. G. (1952) *The advanced theory of statistics (Vol. I)*. New York: Hafner.

Kendall, M. G. (1955) *Rank correlation methods (Second ed.)*. New York: Hafner.

Kruskal, W. H., and Wallis, A. (1952) Use of ranks in one-criterion variance analysis. *J. Amer. Statist. Assn.*, 47, 583–621; see also supplementary note, (1953), 48, 907–911.

Kuder, G. F., and Richardson, M. W. (1937) The theory of the estimation of test reliability. *Psychometrika*, 2, 151–160.

Lindquist, E. F. (1953) *Design and analysis of experiments in psychology and education.* Boston: Houghton Mifflin.

Loevinger, J. (1947) A systematic approach to the construction and evaluation of tests of ability. *Psychol. Monogr.*, 61, No. 4.

Lord, F. M. (1955) Sampling fluctuations resulting from the sampling of test items. *Psychometrika*, 20, 1–22.

Lowry, D. C. (1955) Variance components with reference to genetic population parameters. *Biometrics*, 11, 136–148.

Lyerly, S. B. (1952) The average Spearman rank correlation coefficient. *Psychometrika*, 17, 421–428.

Lykken, D. T. (1956) A method of actuarial pattern analysis. *Psychol. Bull.*, 53, 102–107.

Mahmoud, A. F. (1955) Test reliability in terms of factor theory. *Brit. J. statist. Psychol.*, 8, 119–135.

Marks, E. S. (1947) Sampling in the revision of the Stanford-Binet scale. *Psychol. Bull.*, 44, 413–434.

Marks, E. S. Effects of complex sample designs on tests of significance. (In press.)

Mather, K. (1943) *Statistical analysis in biology.* New York: Interscience Publishers.

McNemar, Q. (1955) *Psychological statistics (Second ed.)* New York: Wiley.

McQuitty, L. L. (1956) Agreement analysis: classifying persons by predominant patterns of responses. *Brit. J. statist. Psychol.*, 9, 5–16.

Meehl, P. E. (1950) Configural scoring. *J. consult. Psychol.*, 14, 165–171.

Merrington, M., and Thompson, C. M. (1943) Tables of percentage points of the inverted beta (F) distribution. *Biometrika*, 33, 73–88.

Mosel, J. N., and Roberts, J. (1954) The comparability of measures of profile similarity: an empirical study. *J. consult. Psychol.*, 18, 61–66.

Nelder, J. A.   (1954) The interpretation of negative components of variance. *Biometrika*, 41, 544–548.

Newman, H. H., Freeman, F. N., and Holzinger, K. J.   (1937) *Twins: A study of heredity and environment*. Chicago: Univ. of Chicago Press.

Osgood, C. E., and Suci, G. J.   (1952) A measure of relation determined by both mean difference and profile information. *Psychol. Bull.*, 49, 251–262.

Pearson, E. S., and Hartley, H. O.   (1956) *Biometrika tables for statisticians, Vol. I*. Cambridge: Cambridge Univ. Press.

Pearson, K., *et al.*   (1901) Mathematical contributions to the theory of evolution. IX: On the principle of homotyposis and its relation to heredity, to variability of the individual, and to that of race. Part I: Homotyposis in the vegetable kingdom. *Philos. Trans. Roy. Soc. (London), Series A*, 197, 285–379.

Pilliner, A. E. G.   (1952) The application of analysis of variance to problems of correlation. *Brit. J. Psychol. (Statis. Sec.)*, 5, 31–38.

Quenouille, M. H.   (1950) Multivariate experimentation. *Biometrics*, 6, 303–316.

Rao, C. R.   (1952) *Advanced statistical methods in biometric research*. New York: Wiley.

Rosen, A.   (1953) Test-retest stability of MMPI scales for a psychiatric population. *J. consult. Psychol.*, 17, 217–221.

Satterthwaite, F. E.   (1941) Synthesis of variance. *Psychometrika*, 6, 309–316.

Satterthwaite, F. E.   (1946) An approximate distribution of estimates of variance components. *Biometrics Bull.*, 2, 110–114.

Scheffé, H.   (1956) A "mixed model" for the analysis of variance. *Ann. math. Statist.*, 27, 23–36.

Schultz, E. F.   (1955) Rules of thumb for determining expectations of mean squares in analysis of variance. *Biometrics*, 11, 123–135.

Schultz, F. G.   (1945) Recent developments in the statistical analysis of ranked data adapted to educational research. *J. exp. Educ.*, 13, 149–152.

Siegel, S.   (1956) *Nonparametric statistics for the behavioral sciences*. New York: McGraw-Hill.

Smith, C. A. B.   (1952–53) The linear function maximizing intraclass correlation. *Ann. Eugenics*, 17, 286–292.

Snedecor, G. W.   (1956) *Statistical methods applied to experiments in agriculture and biology (Fifth ed.)* Ames, Iowa: Iowa State College Press.

Spearman, C.   (1904) The proof and measurement of association between two things. *Amer. J. Psychol.*, 15, 72–101.

Spearman, C.   (1910) Correlation calculated from faulty data. *Brit. J. Psychol.*, 3, 270–295.

"Student"   (1908) The probable error of a mean. *Biometrika*, 6, 1–25.

"Student" (1921) An experimental determination of the probable error of Dr. Spearman's correlation coefficient. *Biometrika*, 13, 263–282.

Tatsuoka, M. M., and Tiedeman, D. V. (1954) Discriminant analysis. *Rev. educ. Res.*, 24, 402–420.

Thorndike, R. L., *et al.* (1951) Reliability. In: Lindquist, E. F., *Educational measurement*. Washington, D. C.: Amer. Council on Educ., Ch. 15, pp. 560–620.

Thurstone, L. L., and Thurstone, T. G. (1941) Factorial studies of intelligence. *Psychometric Monogr.*, No. 2.

Tiedeman, D. V. (1955) On the study of types. *Symposium on pattern analysis*. USAF School of Aviation Medicine, Randolph Field, pp. 1–14.

Treloar, A. E. (1936) *An outline of biometric analysis*. Minneapolis, Minn.: Burgess Publ. Co.

Tryon, R. C. (1957) Reliability and domain validity: reformulation and historical critique. *Psychol. Bull.*, 54, 229–249.

Tukey, J. W. (1951) Components in regression. *Biometrics*, 7, 33–70.

Tyler, F. T. (1951) A factorial analysis of fifteen MMPI scales. *J. consult. Psychol.*, 15, 451–456.

Walker, H. M., and Lev, J. (1953) *Statistical inference*. New York: Holt.

Wallis, W. A. (1939) The correlation ratio for ranked data. *J. Amer. Statist. Assn.*, 34, 533–538.

Wallis, W. A., and Roberts, H. V. (1956) *Statistics: A new approach*. Glencoe, Ill.: Free Press.

Walsh, J. E. (1947) Concerning the effect of intraclass correlation on certain significance tests. *Ann. math. Statist.*, 18, 88–96.

Webster, H. A. (1952) A note on profile similarity. *Psychol. Bull.*, 49, 538–539.

Wechsler, D. (1944) *The measurement of adult intelligence*. Baltimore: Williams and Wilkins.

Wechsler, D. (1955) *Manual for the Wechsler Adult Intelligence Scale*. New York. Psychological Corp.

Wheeler, W. M., Little, K. B., and Lehner, G. F. J. (1951) The internal structure of the MMPI. *J. consult. Psychol.*, 16, 134–141.

Wilk, M. B., and Kempthorne, O. (1955) Fixed, mixed, and random models. *J. Amer. Statist. Assn.*, 60, 1144–1167.

Wissler, C. (1901) The correlation of mental and physical traits. *Psychol. Rev.*, *Monogr. Suppl.*, No. 16.

Woodbury, M. A. (1940) Rank correlation when there are equal variates. *Ann. math. Statist.*, 11, 358–362.

Zubin, J. A. (1937) The determination of response patterns in personality adjustment inventories. *J. educ. Psychol.*, 28, 401–413.

index

INDEX†

Aborn, M., 108, 109
Alexander, H. W., 5
analysis of variance
  assumptions: description and inference, 46, 47
  assumptions: pattern analysis, 99–105
  classifications
    random, fixed, arbitrary, 50–57
    random, from a finite population, 56, 57, 62–67, 86
  models
    and components of variance
      one-way, 52–55; two-way, 39–43, 55–62; three-way, 81–95
    random, mixed, fixed, 39–43, 50–57, 84–95
Anderson, R. L., 33, 47, 49, 52, 55, 57, 58, 60, 95

Bancroft, T. A., 33, 47, 49, 52, 55, 57, 58, 60, 95
BCMS $= 0$ when $K = \infty$ in the population, 69, 70, 101
Benard, A., 134, 137
Bhargava, R. P., 21
Blair, G. M., 64
Block, J., 97

Boas, F., 4
Bock, R. D., 93, 102, 118
Brown, W., 76
Brozek, J., 5
Brunswik, E., 49
Burt, C., 5, 92
Bushard, W. J., 5

Canter, A. H., 108, 109
Cattell, R. B., 97
Chapman, J., 97, 102, 118
χ_r^2 Friedman's test statistic for ranks, 139–141
class membership
  indistinguishability of scores, 3, 30–32, 35–38, 54, 72
  order effect, 36–38, 42
  prediction of, 32–34
Cochran, W. G., 5, 58, 67, 95
components of variance
  rules for estimating, 54, 57, 58, 87
  negative components, 58, 71, 115, 116
confidence interval, 22–26
  vs. level of statistical significance, 24, 25
Coombs, C. H., 5
Cronbach, L. J., 90, 92, 97

---

† See also Glossary for reference to symbols and formulas

Crump, S. L., 58

Danford, M. B., 97
Daniels, H. E., 58
Davis, A., 14
Derner, G. F., 108, 109
du Mas, F. M., 97
Durbin, J., 134

Ebel, R. L., 5
Edwards, A. L., 107, 134
Ehrenberg, A. S. C., 134
Eisenhart, C., 47, 48
Ellson, D. G., 97
Elteren, Ph. van, 134, 137
$E(MS)$ expected mean square, 11, 12, 53 ff., 81 ff., 102–105
estimation
    population parameters, 22–26, 47 ff., 76 ff., 103 ff.
    population value of $\tilde{R}$, 5, 11, 12, 22–26, 34, 47 ff., 76 ff., 103 ff.
    see also components of variance
$\eta_r{}^2$ Wallis' correlation ratio for ranks, 136, 139–141
experimental unit, 47, 48, 94
    randomization of, 56, 57

F Snedecor's test statistic, 19, 23, 38, 60, 64, 65, 89, 94
    tables of, 144–147
F_{ck} test statistic for similarity of profiles, 105
$F_k = F_L$ test statistic for differences among profile levels, 105
F_r test statistic for ranks, 130, 140
fpc finite population correction, 56, 57, 62–67, 86, 94
Ferguson, G. A., 5, 75, 76, 77, 92, 103
Fielder, M., 14
Fieller, E. C., 4
Fisher, R. A., 4, 5, 13, 20, 23, 25, 34, 58, 66, 125
Fraser, D. A. S., 123, 125, 134
Freeman, F. N., 31
Friedman, M., 134, 137, 138, 139

Gaier, E. L., 97
Glaser, R., 103
Gleser, G. C., 97
Gough, H. G., 107
Gulliksen, H., 92, 103
Gupta, H. C., 149
Guttman, L., 92

Haggard, E. A., 47, 75, 91, 97, 102, 118
Hald, A., 20, 26, 58
Hansen, M. H., 5, 67
Harris, J. A., 3, 4, 10, 36, 149
Harris, R. E., 112
Harter, H. L., 49, 55, 57, 58, 95
Hartley, H. O., 20
Hess, R. D., 14
Holt, S. B., 4
Holzinger, K. J., 31
Horst, P., 92, 97, 134
Hotelling, H., 123
Hoyt, C., 5, 92
Hurwitz, W. N., 5, 67

Jackson, R. W. B., 5, 76, 77, 92
Jellinek, E. M., 26
Johnson, P. O., 77
Jonckheere, A. R., 134
Jones, H. E., 31
Jones, M. C., 32

$\bar{k}$ average class membership in a one-way design, 14, 78
Kelley, T. L., 127, 134
Kempthorne, O., 55, 57, 58
Kendall, M. G., 21, 25, 58, 118, 123, 124, 127, 133, 134, 137, 138, 139
Kruskal, W. H., 123, 134, 135
Kuder, G. F., 84, 89, 90, 91, 92, 134

Lee, M. C., 97
Lehner, G. F. J., 107
Lev, J., 125, 134

Levine, L., 97
Lindquist, E. F., 5, 20, 49, 55, 58, 92
Little, K. B., 107
Loevinger, J., 92
Lord, F. M., 90
Lowry, D. C., 58
Lum, M. D., 49, 55, 57, 58, 95
Lyerly, S. B., 127, 134
Lykken, D. T., 97

McNemar, Q., 68, 97
McQuitty, L. L., 97
Madow, W. G., 5, 67
Mahmoud, A. F., 92
Marks, E. S., 5
Mather, K., 36
Mauldin, W. P., 5
Meehl, P. E., 97
Merrington, M., 20
Mosel, J. N., 97
multivariate data and methods, 100, 118–122

Nelder, J. A., 58, 116
Newman, H. H., 31

Osgood, C. E., 97

Pabst, M. R., 123
pattern analysis
  applications
    Minnesota Multiphasic Personality Inventory data, 112–117
    Wechsler-Bellevue data, 108–112
  correlations among subtests, 106–108
  statistical method, 99–105
  S-scores, 104 ff.
  definition of profile, 97
  definitions of pattern, 97–99
  types of patterns, 98
  with groups of persons, 118–122
Pearson, E. S., 20
Pearson, K., 3

Peterson, J. H., 5
Pilliner, A. E. G., 5
profile, definition of, 97
  profile of class means, 99, 122

Quenouille, M. H., 118

R coefficient of intraclass correlation, 11, 12, 14, 17, 19, 38, 54, 59, 60, 64, 65, 71, 72
  asymmetrical distribution, 18, 19
  confidence limits, 22–26
  difference between two R's, 25, 26
  limiting values, 17–19
  negative R's, 18, 19, 21, 22, 70–72
  statistical significance, 19–22, 24, 47–49
  uniformity as a general measure, 6, 7, 94
  see also comparison of R and r or $\bar{r}$
  see also comparison of R and F
$\tilde{R}$ population value of intraclass correlation, 5, 11, 12, 22–26, 34, 47 ff., 76 ff., 103 ff.
R_C coefficient of test unit consistency, 88, 92
$R_C^* = R_{K-R}$ coefficient of test consistency, 89, 92
R_E coefficient of test unit equivalence, 87
R_H Harris' formula for intraclass correlation, 10, 149–151
R_l lower confidence limit of R, 23, 24
R_L intraclass correlation among profile levels, 105
$R_P = 1-R_{ck}$ measure of profile similarity, 70, 105
  statistical significance, 110, 111
R_r intraclass correlation among k rankings, 130, 140
  computation of, 129–134
  properties of, 126–129
  relation to ρ and $\bar{\rho}$, 126, 127
  significance of, 128, 137–139
  tied ranks, effect of, 134–137

R_r* reliability of k rankings, 134

R_S coefficient of test unit stability, 87

R_T coefficient of true test unit reliability, 88, 92

R_T* coefficient of true test reliability, 89 ff.

R_u upper confidence limit of R, 23, 24

R compared with F, 6, 7
  effect of R on test statistics, 5
  experimental vs. observational research, 61, 62, 73, 74
  limiting values, 6, 7, 94
  relation (algebraic), 19–25
  relation (components of variance), 59–61, 88, 94, 95

R compared with r or $\bar{r}$, 7–9, 26–34
  accuracy, 34
  as estimate of reliability, 76–81
  limiting values of R and $\bar{r}$, 19
  order effect, 37
  R_c and $\bar{r}$, 28, 152, 153
  R_H and $\bar{r}$, 26, 151, 152

ranks and rankings
  origins of, 124–125
  ranks vs. measurements, 123–126
  statistics for $c \times k$ matrix, 140
  tied ranks, 134–137

Rao, C. R., 97, 118

reliability
  general discussion, 4, 5, 38–40, 70n
  sources of error variation, 74, 75, 82
  parallel forms, 77, 83, 87 ff., 154–156
  split-half, 76, 77, 84, 88 ff., 154
  test-retest, 75, 77, 83, 84, 87 ff., 154–156
  use of r as an estimate, 76–79
  use of R as an estimate, 79 ff.
  three-parameter case, 76, 77, 154
  four-parameter case, 77, 154–156

Richardson, M. W., 84, 89, 90, 91, 92, 134

Roberts, H. V., 33
Roberts, J., 97
Rosen, A., 113, 114

S-scores, stabilized scores used in pattern analysis, 104 ff.
sample surveys, 3–5, 67
Satterthwaite, F. E., 49, 58, 95
Scheffé, H., 55
Schultz, E. F., 58
Schultz, F. G., 133
Siegel, S., 125, 134
Simonson, E., 5
Smith, B. B., 133, 134, 137, 138, 139
Smith, C. A. B., 4
Snedecor, G. W., 20, 31, 55, 58, 64, 143
Spearman, C., 75, 76, 123
Spearman-Brown prophecy formula, 89 ff., 134
standard error of measurement
  estimated from outside data, 67–69
  use in pattern analysis, 103 ff.
"Student," 11, 127, 135
Suci, G. J., 97
symmetric correlation table, 3, 4, 10, 11, 31

Tatsuoka, M. M., 118
test units, 85
Thompson, C. M., 20
Thorndike, R. L., 75, 92
Thurstone, L. L., 119
Thurstone, T. G., 119
Tiedeman, D. V., 97, 118
Treloar, A. E., 4
Tryon, R. C., 92
Tukey, J. W., 30, 58
Tyler, F. T., 107

unequal k means and variances, effect on R, 29, 30, 78

W Kendall and Smith's coefficient of concordance for ranks, 136, 140–141
Walker, H. M., 125, 134

Wallis, W. A., 33, 123, 133, 134, 135, 140
Walsh, J. E., 5
Webster, H. A., 97
Wechsler, D., 107, 108, 111
Wheeler, W. M., 107
Wilk, M. B., 55, 57

Wissler, C., 39, 75, 76
Woodbury, M. A., 137

Yates, F., 125

Zubin, J. A., 97